THE INGRID PITT BOOK OF
MURDER,
TORTURE & DEPRAVITY

B. T. BATSFORD · LONDON

My special thanks to Barry McCann, MA, for all his help with the research

Text © Ingrid Pitt 2000

A catalogue record for this book is available from the British Library.

ISBN 0 7134 8676 7

Printed in Great Britain by Butler and Tanner Ltd, Frome and London

Volume © B T Batsford 2000
A member of the Chrysalis Group plc

First published in 2000 by
B T Batsford
9 Blenheim Court
Brewery Road
London N7 9NT

Contents

Introduction

Murder's easy! It requires no ingenious business plan, no bank account, no partners, no education and no particular skills. It doesn't even need physical strength. Nor a plan. It is a fact that the majority of murders are committed within the family unit. Usually in a fit of violent pique. The drip, drip, drip of marital discord, jealous rivalry between siblings, greed, the desperation of a single parent unable to cope or something as casual as a hasty word can light the fuse that results in a bloody reaction. Although this is not excusable, it is understandable. The murderers, torturers and depraved sadists who follow had three things in common. They knew what they were doing, enjoyed it and were happy to repeat the experience whenever the mood took them.

Not all who committed the ultimate crime were considered law breakers. Some had the comfort of being the law maker, the law giver. Caligula was told by his grandmother, Antonia, right from the start, that when she had carved her bloody course through those closer to the throne, he would be the ultimate power in the land. Caligula might have turned out to be a liberal Caesar if he hadn't suffered a personality-changing illness. But then everyone can 'if' their life; the only thing that matters in the end is what is remembered. Caligula is remembered as an insane monster. Thomas de Torquemada is another who thought he had the right to torture and murder. A divine as well as a secular right. He had the blessing of the Pope to imprison and torture anybody who crossed his path and the strong arm of the rulers of

Spain, Ferdinand and Isabella, to order death in the most hideous manner his febrile brain could conjure up. Until Tomas arrived on the scene, the Inquisition had been a tribunal that the insecure Catholic church could use to discipline waverers among the congregation and clergy. His handbook for Inquisitors, issued with the full approval of Pope Sixtus in 1482, covered the treatment of anyone coming within the scope of the retribution arm of the church. It makes grim reading.

There are others that were paid by the authorities to do their dirty work for them. The position of Public Executioner was a job that drew many suspect characters to it. Jack Ketch became the nickname for a hangman or bungled execution. He, like many others in the trade, finished up on the gallows of his apprentice. The job tended to go to members of a family in succession. The Pierrepoints were not only the most recent but the last family to knot the noose in the UK. Between them, Harry, Tom and Albert did away with around 1000 poor souls trusted to their fearful gallows. In spite of the well of experience they brought to the job, not all their executions were conducted with swift efficiency. Albert had the highest tally with a score well in the 600s. He was even brought in when the American Master Sergeant signed to hang the Nazi war criminals at Nüremberg fell down on the job. The work load was immense but, it is alleged, Pierrepoint still had time to dally with Irma Grese – The Beautiful Blonde Beast of Belsen.

Maybe Alexander Pearce had little choice when he slew and ate his companions. It was a dog eat dog situation and Alex had the last yelp. Nazi Major Otto Dickmann was an intelligent man. Bit of a *bon vivant*. But he stood by and watched his men burn down the little French village of Oradour-sur-Glane on a warm summer's day without a flicker of remorse. Nobody escaped from the church and barn where the troopers had imprisoned them. The gutted village stands to this day as a memorial to the mindless violence he unleashed. Greed spurred Marcel Petiot into building a killing house in Paris at the height of German occupation. There he lured Jews and others on the Gestapo extermination list with promises of salvation. So many listened to his promises that his efficient abattoir broke down and the smell of decomposing bodies brought about his exposure.

The scene in the Marr household in London's Whitechapel when the Bow Street Runners arrived was so sickening that the phlegmatic officers found it hard to cope. The murderer, John Williams, would have got away with it if he hadn't gone on to repeat his hideous crime only a week or so later – and in the same area. A man who no amount of blood and gore would have inconvenienced was Marshal of France Gilles de Rais, one time bosom buddy of the Maid of Orleans, Jeanne d'Arc. He threw orgies for his friends, neighbours and visiting Ecclesiastes that were the talk of medieval France. Boys were his thing and he is said to have used them, suitably fitted with a spigot and suspended above the dining table, to obtain his favourite tipple, warm blood. Everything was fine until he ran out of money. Then he really found out who among his depraved drinking pals were his real friends.

Among these educated and powerful men, the Scottish cannibal Sawney Bean appears a pathetic creature. He was ill-educated and under the thumb of a domineering wife. If they had never met, he would probably have spent his life ploughing other people's fields and spawning another generation of farm labourers. His children, all 50 odd of them, counting the in-bred grandchildren, were innocent. They murdered and ate as many travellers who crossed their path as their parents but they, at least, were cut off from the mores and laws of society from birth. In the end, they suffered the same hideous fate as their culpable elders.

The man who spawned a flood of feature films, Ed Gein, from a backwoods dirt farm in Wisconsin, had a mother fixation. When she died, he was on the loose. He wanted to dominate the women that paid scant notice of him as he went about his everyday life. The State Agricultural plan, which paid him not to work his farm, must also share the blame. As the old saying goes: the Devil makes work for idle hands. And Ed's hands worked overtime slaughtering, skinning and preserving the interesting body parts of his victims. Another murderer, from the neighbouring State of Indiana, Belle Gunness, an ex-Carnie performer, just wanted stability. That meant money. So she applied a business-like approach and advertised for a husband. The line of men beating a path to her door, pockets bulging with dollars, either says something about the stupidity of men or the power of advertising. None of them escaped Belle's bloody axe and burial in the pig pen. Did she get away with it? That is the basis for an on-going argument.

George Neville Heath was an ex-Air Force officer. He was drummed out of everything from the cubs to the Royal Air Force but it didn't dent his self-confidence, especially where women were concerned. Women were easily taken in by his blonde good looks and charming manner. Along the way he slept with one too many good time girls and caught a dose of syphilis. His penchant for a little rough foreplay turned to murder and his self-confidence put him in the frame for a dawn meeting with Albert Pierrepoint. Jealousy was Dr Geza de Kaplann's driving force. He couldn't take the attention his beautiful Hungarian wife attracted so he decided to disfigure her so that nobody else fancied her. He well deserved the soubriquet of Doctor Acid.

These are just a few of the monsters that are examined in my book of *Murder, Torture and Depravity*. How do they measure up on the yard stick of that old sweetie from Hungary, Countess Erzebet Bathory, who is credited with murdering, torturing and generally acting in a decidedly depraved manner with over 650 virgins? Very favourably. So let's start with her.

1

Countess Erzebet Bathory

Countess Bathory's position in the hierarchy of horror is confused by the fact that she, along with Vlad Tepes and Gilles de Rais, is credited as being one of the progenitors of the Vampire myth. None of them passes the basic test for a vampire of being dead and reanimated. Their reputation as seminal vampires rests entirely on their penchant for groping around in the blood of their victims. Not one of them was actually seen or accused of sucking the blood straight from the vein. This may have been an oversight on the part of the chronicler or something that hadn't occurred to the trio of blood bandits. Vlad's only claim to vampire-hood was made by Bram Stoker using the Prince of Transylvania's family name for the anti-hero of his book, *Dracula*. A brilliant connection if you are hoping that nobody is going to be bothered by the truth. de Rais' hook into the legend of the vampire is even more tenuous. He was just a pervert who liked torturing and disembowelling young boys.

Countess Bathory's problem is that she has been left in a sort of horror limbo. Overqualified as a ghoul, she is usually shuffled into the wrong nomenclature and gets a vampire label. This has not been helped by the Hammer film, *Countess Dracula*. It is the connection to Bram Stoker and his eponymous hero that is the trouble. The Countess could possibly have had some distant claim to the family of Dracul if she hadn't already claimed the Nadasdy name by marriage. The storyline goes that Erzebet is a headstrong young maiden of a royally connected family who marries an older man and goes off the rails when the Count fails to perform his marital duties and prefers swanning off to places foreign for a bit of pillage and murder with the odd act of rape for afters. Erzebet develops a liking for disciplining servants that gets a little out of hand. Her come-uppance is being walled up in the cellar of her castle where she dies of starvation shortly after.

Naturally this isn't colourful enough for a full-length feature film with the Hammer logo riding on it, so a more erotic plot was hatched. The old girl isn't too happy spending good servant-baiting time trying to iron out the wrinkles that the years insisted on etching into her previously marbled features. In a vicious tussle with one of her unfortunate employees she cuts the poor girl's face and blood spurts out and splashes on to the Countess. She's not too happy with that until she looks in the mirror and sees that where the blood splattered her cheek it has become miraculously peach-like. Quick as a flash she realises that all she has to do to remain the juvenile lead forever is to apply the bloodied bodies of virgin servants to her wrinkled skin. This she does until the locality is running seriously short of suitable maidens and her nurse introduces the blood of a local lady of the tavern into her bubble bath. This is not efficacious and Erzebet is severely pissed off. Into the household comes Ilona, the Countess's pulchritudinous daughter who is, at least so it is assumed, a virgin, in spite of a decidedly suspect cohabitation in a very basic hovel in the forest with a wood-chopper. The Countess is about to marry the love of her old age, handsome and somewhat soppy young cavalry officer, Imre Toth, when her old age revisits her with a vengeance. Toth doesn't mind the idea of a mother figure but blanches at the idea of a grandmother figure in his bed. The Countess goes potty and tries to liberate a little virgin blood from her daughter to recapture her youth. Her youth, Toth, in a daze, manages to stand between mother and daughter and catches a knife in the ribs to be going on with. Then various members of Erzebet's extended family jump on her and sling her in a cellar. The appellation 'Countess Dracula' comes from a woman whose husband has just been crushed when he carelessly fell under the wheels of the Countess's carriage as she is speeding back to the castle for Sunday lunch. In wild-eyed desperation the newly created widow damns Bathory and upstages Stoker by dramatically screaming after the speeding carriage the immortal words – Countess Dracula.

This is the generally accepted film version. The truth is more horrific but a generally accepted depiction of real-life ghoulish goings-on in a medieval castle in the forests of Romania. Where the Countess was born is a matter of little importance, although it is usually accepted that it was Bratislava in the Slovak Republic in 1560. At that time national boundaries were as amorphous as a jellyfish in a whirlpool. Her family were rich and connected to King Stephen of Poland and the Prince of Transylvania. Childhood was a round of property owned by the Bathory family and visited as often as possible to make sure that shifty neighbours weren't shifting the boundary posts. Servants were considered more expendable than cattle and of far less value than a horse. And sex wasn't something furtive and done out of sight of the family. By the time she was a pretty 13, she was taking her pick of the lustier servants. It might have put a smile on the face of a gardener when she enticed him into the potting shed but it soon faded when she had him dragged out and beaten. Her marriage to the ageing Boyar, Count Ferenz Nadasdy, at the tempting age of 15 was about par for that distant course but didn't fulfil Erzebet's dreams of romantic love. She was intelligent, forceful and well educated. She knew what was what and knew she wasn't getting it. Nadasdy, now that the boring nuptials were out of the way, his teenage bride had a dumpling in the

pot and his family was bound to the powerful Bathory family, bid a fond farewell and left for conquests new. To while away the hours between serf savaging and dinner, Erzebet took over the running of the estate. This was not looked on as a suitable occupation for a young bride and produced a considerable humph factor among her male relatives, especially a cousin, Count George Thurzo. Sitting in his draughty room, he worked himself into a state of belief that assumed that the fortune of his young cousin should, by right of testes, be his. The Countess did not think much of her seedy cousin and left him to fend for himself. This meant that he went off to his other cousin, the King, and spent a few years whispering into the royal ear-trumpet the iniquities of their wealthy cousin. Erzebet was exactly that – a wealthy cousin – with powerful allies within her family group. Too powerful for a monarch beset with dynastic problems and the disconcerting knowledge that the marauding Turks would love the opportunity to leap in, swords akimbo, if he were foolish enough to take his eye off the orb for a few seconds to take on the Bathory/Nadasdy combined. Especially as his only ally was likely to be the wimpish Thurzo. So the King listened and nodded and Thurzo whined and whimpered and the Countess grew older and more powerful.

As Lord Acton wrote to the Bishop, 'Power tends to corrupt and absolute power corrupts absolutely'. And this was Erzebet's problem. With no one to stop her, she moved rapidly into the absolute corruption phase without the spectre of going to jail and not collecting 200 smackers to stop her. Seducing gardeners and whipping recalcitrant servants had become a chore. She needed something extra to stimulate her juices. Then she met Anna Darvulia. Anna was a nurse with an eye to an opportunity when it bit her. In intimate chats between deep massage and colonic irrigation she learned a lot about her employer. Enough to suggest some interesting variations on flogging and pinching. It started quite slowly. A forgetful servant was sat on white hot coals to help her future memory. Maids who didn't warm the bed

Countess Dracula showers in the blood of virgins.

before the Countess retired were stripped, doused with water and made to stand out in the courtyard until they died or bits of their anatomy froze off. Erzebet hadn't enjoyed herself so much since she had a coachman castrated for breaking a wheel and causing her head to come into sharp contact with the side of the coach. She urged Anna to think up more turns to stave off the monotony of daily life in the castle. The Nurse duly obliged with ear clipping, breast squashing, nose slitting and various excruciatingly painful attacks on the genital organs. These were carried out by the servants and Anna while Erzebet looked on and encouraged. Voyeurism wasn't as exciting as the real thing and it wasn't long before the Countess herself was practising some of the subtleties of torture under the watchful eye of the resourceful Nurse. Up until this time it had all been fairly restrained and not much different from what was practised in other households before the age of Tuppaware and TV. Then Count Ferenz went an orgy too far and croaked. Liberated from any restraint, Erzebet now became the leader rather than the acolyte in Nurse Darvulia's little *soirees*. Wisely, she had left the male members of her staff out of her fests and used them as willing allies in her chastisement and correction of ungrateful female staff. She was glad she had because the work of debauchery was heavy and not fitting for the daughter of nobility. While Anna scoured the countryside for suitable women, in the virgin category, the men were instructed in building the apparatus of torture. Very popular at this time was the Iron Maiden. A coffin-like arrangement very much like the sarcophagus of a Pharaoh. With one unpleasant extra. The interior was fitted out with long, sharp spikes. The Countess liked the basic concept but failed to see how it would benefit her. Once the hinged door was closed the victim was out of sight. Out of sight meant she might as well go to bed, and the exciting potential of her cellar made it very difficult to sleep. The thought of missing so much excitement gave her a headache and made her ratty. Nurse Anna couldn't have that. 'How about building an open cage and…' Erzebet loved the idea and set her workman on to building a metal box about five feet tall and four feet square. Into the sides were welded sharp spikes like those used in the Iron Maiden. This was going to be the grand finale to which everything would build. As the venerable Beaton was later to say, 'First catch your bunny'. No problem. Anna produced a pink young female for the approval of her mistress. Approval was granted with a courtly nod of the head. Seized by the men the hapless woman was stripped and laid on a table. With immaculate precision Erzebet then performed the overture. Ear-clipping, eyelid snipping, nose slitting, eyeball gouging, breast cutting, red hot poker up the vagina or anus and anything else that came to mind. She had to be careful. Sometimes after she had exhausted herself preparing for the finale, the ungrateful recipient of her attention would inconveniently die and she would have to start from the beginning again. But practice made perfect and before long she was able to judge to a snip what any of her performers could take and still provide an entertaining grand finale.

The girl was helped into the spiked cage, making sure that she needn't carelessly impale herself on any of the spikes, and the cage lifted aloft. A comfortable chair was then placed under the cage and the Countess helped to her seat. When she was settled the men were given the nod. From a conveniently placed brazier they took burning embers and thrust them at the caged woman. In her attempt to get away from the fire she impaled herself on the sharp spikes. Before long the blood was cascading down on the Countess. She moaned and writhed around in orgasmic fever until the blood ceased to flow. She would then courteously thank those present for the spectacle and repair to her chamber. In the cellar the servants cleaned up and prepared whatever delight Anna thought up for the next day. As far as the Countess was concerned everything was right with the world. Cousin Thurzo was still moping around trying to figure out how he could get his hands on her loot, even helping out in the cellar on occasions, but he couldn't find anything untoward that would make the King step in and restore to him what he was sure was rightfully his. Then Anna Darvulia inconveniently caught a bug and died. The Countess was disconsolate. Who would look after her now? Who would provide the ingredients for her entertainment and sexual delight now? She need not have worried. Anna had a part-time assistant, a local farmer's wife called Erzsi Majorosne. She hadn't Anna's delicacy and sophistication but she knew the ropes and was willing to learn. While Anna had been alive, the local supplies of woman eligible to take part in the performances of the Countess had been stretched to the limit. Darvulia had always been careful to use only women that had been bonded to the Countess. Brought willingly to the castle by their starving mothers and sold into bondage for a few coppers. The ignorance of farmer's wife Majorosne now became fatally apparent. Pushed for time she came across a couple of girls ripe for the sport. They weren't bonded servants and their clothes and accents did suggest that they might not be good serf material but Majorosne had already been promised a lead part in the proceedings if things didn't work out so she was in no mood to be fussy. The girls put on a noble performance. The Countess thanked Majorosne and the future seemed set to fair.

Then the families of the young ladies of breeding began to get anxious at their no-show around the baronial hearth. Thurzo got to hear about it and quickly counted his fingers and came up with the answer that his dear cousin had, at last, overstepped the boundaries of polite behaviour. A new king was now in power, King Mathias. Since his early days in court Thurzo had learned a lot about brown-nosing and this time he approached his sovereign more circumspectly. Mathias was susceptible to flattery and accepted that he was too bright a ruler to have his powerful noble families rampaging around the country playing games with each other. Count Thurzo suggested that the crown of Mathias would shine more brightly with the Bathory lands in the hands of a member of the noble family who

was totally loyal to the King. The King agreed – with provisos. Thurzo had to have a case that would stand up in open court. How he put the case together was not something to attract Regal consideration. Thurzo assured his liege lord that there would be no whitewash in the woods, leaped aboard his trusty steed and made tracks for Cachtice Castle where Countess Bathory had now established her household.

The Countess was hard put to be civil to her irritatingly servile cousin but had no fear that he could harm her in any way. A bad mistake. By bribery and threats he got the truth from the castle servants. He promised Erzsi Majorosne amnesty if she confessed and told him everything. Erzsi realised that she had made a bit of a bloomer. Even if she managed to fob Thurzo off, it would probably be reported back to her Mistress by somebody currying favour. Erzsi Majorosne had no illusions about what would happen then. Seeing Majorosne metaphorically spilling her guts, the men were eager not to be left behind. Thurzo promised them that if they put the knife in they could plead that they were forced to do what the Countess bid. They would be given the chance to tell how they had begged and pleaded with her to stop her cruel practices but she had taken no notice. Once the evidence was garnered Thurzo triumphantly spread it out before King Mathias. The King still wasn't exactly pleased to be put on the spot. If the powerful despotic Lady pulled in a few favours, he could still see himself as the Aunt Sally that a coalition of feral barons might find it advantageous to knock down. He was lucky. Countess Bathory had never been a one to tread lightly and win friends. What's more, since she had become interested in the fatiguing business of disciplining her bonded servants full time, she had little appetite for the social round. Thurzo rode back to Cachtice at the head of a troop of the Kings men and arrested his cousin for the kidnap, torture and murder of various spinsters of the parish. It was a fair cop. But Thurzo's interest in what went on in the privacy of his cousin's castle was only a means to a coup. Many of Erzebet's family were in high places. Some had even converted to Catholicism. Others had proven less than supportive of the ruling Habsburgs. Thurzo persuaded Mathias that, given the power, he could act as whipper-in and get the wayward lords back in the kennel. The king believed he was the man for the job and made him Palatine of Hungary. A sort of High Sheriff with knobs on. Thurzo was lucky. It was 1610 and the world of the forests and mountains was in turmoil. Boyars, who would have leaped to the defence of Lord Nadasdy's widow a few years earlier, were too busy watching their own back to spare a glance in her direction. She was summoned to a court in Vasvar-Szombathely to explain the death of the daughter of one of her ladies in waiting. The Lady herself accompanied the Countess and swore on oath that her child had been the victim of disease and had not died from the predations of her employer. Her plea was allowed and Erzebet returned to the cold comforts of her nearest castle. But the very fact that she had been submitted to the indignity of appearing in court gave warning of her unaccustomed vulnerability. Thurzo was quick to urge others to test the Lady of Cachtice. He had chosen his moment and once the defences of her power had been breached – and seen to be breached – there were plenty of witnesses coming forward to point the finger. Thurzo the Palatine was a fury of activity. He could see the rich Bathory lands dropping into his hands like ripe bananas. He didn't hang about. Countess Bathory was brought to court again and the evidence trotted out. But the old girl wasn't finished yet. She orchestrated a series of bluffs that were feasible enough to have the King and Court wondering if they could really come out ahead if they bucked the defendant's extended family. The hearing just sort of fizzled out and the Countess moved back into her castle at Nemetkeresztur. Fear of the reprisals that failure could visit upon him spurred cousin Thurzo into immediate action. He out-pimpled the Scarlet Pimpernel by being here, there and everywhere in a rabid attempt to raise support and not be seen as a sitting target. Vienna,

Budapest, Bratislava, anywhere there was a witness to be bought or a discontent suborned. Soon he felt secure enough to take another pot-shot at the old lady and claim what was his. Now he had evidence that in her depravity Erzebet had slaughtered, for her own amusement, between 600 and 650 virgins. A risible claim. In a township of little more than 4000 earthy souls with little more to do on a steamy summer's night than cool off in the surrounding forests. Where was anyone going to line up 650 virgins? The figure was not seriously challenged and the trial went ahead. One by one Countess Bathory's servants and accomplices took the stand and put the boot in. They were all careful to ascribe the part they had played in the orgies as being a direct result of dire threats of what would happen to them if they didn't co-operate. Some of it might have even been true. They were well aware of what the old ogre was capable of doing, they were actually doing it to others, on her direct orders. In the end it made little difference. Once they had told their story they were detained and sentenced to death. It was a fate even the King was too scared to place on the head of Countess Bathory. In a fine example of fence-building, he made pacts with her sons and daughters, aunts and uncles. The Bloody Countess would be spared, her lands, at least those not held by the fiercer members of her family, would come under the administration of Palatine Thurzo and the Lady herself would be placed under house arrest under the authority of the aforesaid Palatine. What Countess Bathory thought about all of this is not recorded. It is obvious that she knew that sooner or later she was going to get it in the neck. Long before any effort was made to marginalise her and seize her lands, she made sure that some of her prize possessions had been farmed out to her children. Thurzo made a half-hearted attempt to get some of them back but their father, the fearsome Count Ferenz Nadasdy hadn't been called the 'Black Bey' for nothing. The children he had sired had a heady cocktail of savage blood in their veins and weren't in the mood to lose land as well as mother.

So Countess Erzebet Bathory-Nadasdy started a luxurious house arrest in one of her castles that had meant so much to her, Castle Cachtice. Her incarceration was not to last long. She died, probably of boredom, in 1614.

The death of the Countess was not the end of the affair. At first there was a fairly united effort to bury her misdeeds along with the body. For 100 years she was a non-person. Even factions that had an interest in destroying the Bathory name didn't take advantage of many of the opportunities on offer. Then everybody wanted to get on the roller-coaster. As the 18th Century opened so did the Bathory file. Many cast doubt on her guilt, claiming that it was all a big fit-up by her enemies. Others claimed that the figure for those she tortured to death was much lower than the vaunted 650. Fifty maybe – and lower class – so what did it matter? Others ventured the figure much higher, suggesting a probable 1000 or more. Even the Brothers Grimm got into the act with an arithmetical baker's dozen. Opinions change about her psychological make-up. At the time that she was working her murderous magic she was just seen as an old biddy with time on her hands looking for a little X-certificate entertainment who ran foul of the law.

Later it was put down to brain fever. Then it became an unfortunate side effect of a menopausal despot with bloodlust. Freudians opined, naturally, that it was all down to sexual abuse in her childhood. As her early life is a dark valley to researchers, it is a good place to look for the reasons she set out to become the world's, alleged, foremost female serial killer. The fanciful story that she washed daily in the blood of the virgins that she kept in serried ranks in the cellar, like vats of good wine, for her daily ablutions is a little hard to take and begs a whole load of questions. The fact that they had to be virgins adds a twist of piquancy to the story but what could be the difference between the blood of a virgin and some old hooker who plied her trade down at the docks for a Fisherman's Friend and a finger of shag? I guess nobody will know the true story of what happened in darkest Europe 400 years ago but in the meantime, the legend grows and multiplies and books and films are made that suit the age and the pocket of the financiers. It is left to us to imagine what the Countess herself thought about the way she was treated and whether, if guilty, she had any remorse about the lives she had terminated so mercilessly.

2
Neville Heath

In 1946 the world was full of heroes. Ordinary men and women who had gone to war and found themselves in a position to perform an extraordinary act. It was also the time of the Black Market, bombed buildings and those same ordinary heroes trying to re-adjust to a world that no longer appreciated the qualities that had made them more than their component parts. In the main the returning servicemen shrugged and joined the ranks of the underpaid. For some the thought of returning to the dross of civilian life wasn't possible. They had been taught to kill and to get what they wanted by force of arms. A cocktail that was hard to pour back in the shaker. Neville George Clevely Heath had been an officer if not quite a gentlemen in the Royal Air Force. He cut a dashing figure as a Squadron Leader until he was surprised while wearing a DFC without actually being handed this prestigious award by His Majesty. There had also been a bit of nastiness over a gambling debt and the Mess Sergeant put the boot in about items that had gone missing while Heath was duty officer. It was a blow to Heath. He liked being a part of the RAF and enjoyed the privileges that his rank brought him. The Battle of Britain was still fresh in the memory of those who had endured the nightly bombings only curtailed by the warrior efforts of the boys in blue, Churchill's famous Few. Heath played up his part in the Battle for all he was worth. It was a time when wearing a uniform in public was still acceptable and Heath had added a couple of rings of rank to his sleeve and more decorations which he was sure that he was entitled to but had been denied him by jealous senior officers. As Group Captain Heath, top button on his tunic left meticulously undone to show his revered standing as 'One of The Few', his blonde wavy hair just a rakish half an inch longer than the norm, his heavily good-looking features and his cultured, lazy way of speaking set many a heart a flutter. Money was a problem but he had a string of elegant lady friends willing to help him over a sticky patch. Like Billy Bunter, he was always waiting for a postal order to arrive and bail him out. His only real problem was a 'dose' he had caught from one of the ladies who had given him more than the price of the hotel room. Heath found the whole idea of going to a VD Clinic and revealing to pretty nurses he had been furnished with a virulent case of pox an impossible embarrassment. Anyway, he was satisfied that the home cures he had first heard about in the forces had been efficacious. Most of the sores had gone completely and the others were drying up nicely.

His Group Captain guise was wearing thin. He wasn't the only ex-officer wandering around in a rapidly fraying uniform trying to repeat the buzz that deferential treatment in restaurants and the salutes of 'erks' and 'squaddies' brought on. He wasn't even the only ex-service man wearing rank and decorations that hadn't been commissioned. But he was one of the few who persisted in maintaining a high profile. After a couple of close shaves with inquisitive military policemen he decided to cross over to another service and it was as Lt Colonel Heath that met Marjorie Gardner. Marjorie had recently joined the ranks of 'peace-widows', women that had married a gallant serviceman and waved him goodbye when he went off to fight the foe. The out-of-touch civilian that returned was not what she wanted and

Neville Heath slaughters the luckless Doreen Marshall on the moonlit clifftops.

after a short period of doing her duty for the returning boys, she moved out. After all, she was a budding film-star and he was only another bewildered ex-serviceman in a cheap demob suit with a future that fell well short of her expectations. There were still a lot of 'clubs' in London. A legacy from the time when men on leave wanted a taste of the exotic and somewhere they could pull a bird without having to trawl the back streets or stand in line under Waterloo Bridge. When Lt Colonel Heath entered the Panama Club and stood by the bar looking around in his lazy, heavy-lidded manner, Marjorie knew that a new phase in her life was about to start. Heath was all she expected. A witty, cultured George Sanders-type who was obviously bowled over by her beauty and position as a film-star. A couple of hours later they booked in at the Pembridge Court Hotel. It didn't take long for Marjorie to find out that her gentleman friend was anything but. Marjorie Gardner was into bondage before rubber suits and a visit to Anne Summers' emporium was a prior requisite. And there was nothing Neville Heath liked more than a little heavy-handed flagellation – as long as he was wielding the whip. At first glance it looked like a union, if not exactly made in hell, at least just outside the portals. The party began quite amicably. Heath ripped off Marjorie's clothes and she shredded his back with her carefully manicured nails. Excited, Heath quickly bound her arms and legs to the bedposts and started flicking her with his whip. As he became aroused the flicks became full blows. Marjorie's gurgles of enjoyment changed to cries of pain. She begged her lover to stop. Heath replied by gagging her. Now he was so far gone that he could not control himself. He beat her until her body was a welter of blood. Then he fell on her and bit lumps of her flesh and tore chunks from her body. Thankfully, she lapsed into unconsciousness. Sated, Heath sat back and surveyed the room. It looked like a charnel house. Slowly, he got up, cut Marjorie's hands free and felt her pulse. Unbelievably, it was still present. Heath was rapidly regaining control of his thought processes. He

had to get away. He quickly washed himself down, carefully brushed his crisp blond hair, packed his bags and departed the scene. It was left to the maid to find Marjorie. She was dead. Not from the terrible wounds Heath had inflicted but suffocated by the gag in her mouth. It didn't need Poirot to connect Heath with the murder. The police did not release a photograph of him to the newspapers but circulated it to Police Stations throughout the country.

Heath was shocked by what had happened. He had always been happy with a degree of brutality in his love-making but he had always drawn back from inflicting any real injury. It was time to try to cover his tracks. He booked in at the Tollard Royal Hotel in Bournemouth as Captain Rupert Brooke. It suited him to connect himself to the romantic First World War poet who died on the Greek island of Skyros en route to the Dardanelles in 1915. 'Stands the church clock at ten to three? And is there honey still for tea?' and all that. Once settled in, he rang Yvonne Symonds, an ex-WREN he had met a few months earlier at the Overseas Club in London. She had been ill and was staying with her parents by the sea to recuperate. Yvonne was not the easy lay that the Captain was looking for. He wined and dined her but she still wouldn't come across so he asked her to marry him. She was thrilled. The idea was to keep the engagement secret until Heath had been able to sort a few things out and receive the money owed him by the government and various other people who had borrowed from him. Yvonne was happy to lend him a small sum of money when he told her he had an appointment with the War Office to finalise the amount of pension due to him. He promised to repay her as soon as he came back from London. He also mentioned that while he was in the capital he had been asked to drop into Scotland Yard and have a word with the police. When Yvonne pushed him for more information he explained that a room he had been renting in London had been the scene for a particular horrendous murder and the police wanted some help in tracking down the

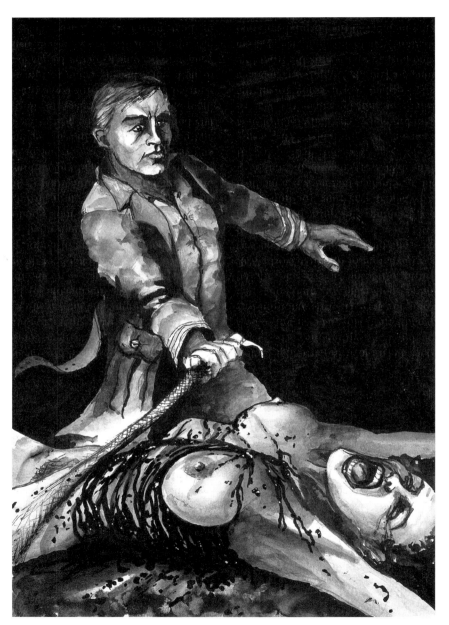

Whipping – Heath's sadistic hallmark.

murderer. He left the following morning but instead of taking the express to London he moved along the coast to Worthing where he sat and wrote a muddled letter to Chief Superintendent Barratt giving his version of what had happened in the Pembridge Hotel. He claimed that he had met Miss Gardner in the club but instead of taking her back to the hotel had loaned her his room. She had told him that she was being forced to meet a man that night and had promised Heath that she would be free by about 3am. If he came back after that, they could spend the rest of the night together. He had been happy to help out as he had promised to play cards at an illegal gaming house and was not using the room. When he returned he found Miss Gardner in the condition in which the police found her. He panicked, gathered up his clothes and beat it before he could get involved in the indelicate affair. In his haste he had inadvertently picked up the whip that had been used to beat the unfortunate woman. This he would forward so that they could check it for fingerprints. Barratt already knew that one of the pieces of evidence he had to find was a riding crop. A criss-cross pattern on the weals covering Marjorie's body were typically those found on a leather riding crop. From the postmark on the letter he was able to make the brilliant deduction that the helpful Heath was on the south coast. Local stations were informed and inquiries intensified. The Superintendent was not surprised when a long, slim parcel did not arrive.

Group Captain Brooke called Yvonne Symonds and told her the whole nasty business at the Pembridge Hotel had now been cleared up to the satisfaction of Scotland Yard and she invited him down for Sunday lunch with her parents. Heath agreed. What he saw as his coup of putting the police off the scent made him feel invulnerable. How much of this was a psychological disorder and what effects tertiary syphilis had on his mental outlook are unknown. But he was acting like a man who should

be leaping off tall building wearing his pants over his tights and yammering on about the American Way.

Lunchtime roast beef and the attention of the adoring Yvonne induced Heath to give the Symonds a graphic and egocentrically tailored account of the brutal murder and his meeting with the police. He cast himself as a latter day Sherlock Holmes pointing out to the stupid police clues that were obvious to a man of his intellect. His description of how something big and hard had been shoved up her wotsit, 'a poker probably' was enough to put his hosts off their apple pie and custard. He bid the shocked family goodbye and returned to his hotel. Just why he felt he had to relate the murder in all its gory details is hard to understand. Was it just bravado? The need to show someone how clever he was? Or was he really insane and living in some fantasy world where he saw his actions as reasonable and a suitable subject for conversation around the Sunday joint? A few weeks later the Symonds were to read a less graphic but painfully similar account of Marjorie Gardner's last moments in the *News of the World*.

Within a couple of days he had a new target in sight. A pretty 21-year-old who had a bob or two and wasn't averse to being fawned over by the gallant war-hero, Doreen Marshall. Courtship was along familiar lines. He engineered an introduction as she returned from a walk along the sea front. After a pleasant afternoon chatting in the conservatory she agreed to have dinner with him. He regaled her with tales of derring-do over the white cliffs of Dover during Britain's 'finest hour'. When she was suitably impressed he encouraged her to talk about herself. She was smitten but when he asked her to stay the night she remembered what her mother had told her about one-night stands and declined graciously. Heath appeared to take her dismissal without rancour and offered to walk her back to her hotel. It was a warm, moonlit night and the romantic in Doreen pushed her into a fatal decision. That walk along the cliff-tops was her last. In a deserted strip of scrub Jekyll turned Hyde. Seemingly careless of anyone accidentally discovering

Neville Heath under arrest. (Popperfoto)

him. he leaped on the unsuspecting woman and threw her into the rhododendron bushes. Doreen was a strong, healthy woman but Heath's insane strength made her powerless to resist. He stripped off her clothes and tried to have intercourse with her. When this failed he tied her hands and holding her penned down by the weight of his body, tore at her like a ravenous animal. Both her nipples were bitten off, her nose half severed and huge chunks of flesh ripped from her body. She pleaded with him to stop but he was beyond reason. He broke off a branch from the bush that was hiding them from view and cruelly rammed it repeatedly into her vagina. Doreen was now on the point of collapse, she was barely conscious and unable to defend herself in any way. Heath pulled out a bone-handled castrating knife, sharp-bladed and long. In a frenzy he plunged it into her vagina and then sawed a terrible slit up through her stomach to her breasts. Demented with blood lust he sat on her blooded body and lashed indiscriminately at her head. In spite of her dreadful injuries she tried to wrest the knife from him. The pain as the sharp blade shredded her fingers was unfelt as she slipped into unconsciousness. A further two gashes from her breasts to her stomach practically cut her in two. But still he wasn't finished. He hacked violently at her throat almost severing her head from her body. He then picked up a large stone and repeatedly smashed it down on her head. Exhausted, Heath sat back and marvelled at his handiwork. He picked up Doreen's clothes and dropped them over her poor tortured body. He stood in the moonlight and looked at the ravages his frenzied attack had made to his usually immaculate attire. If he was spotted, the game would be up before he had a chance to cover his track. Keeping to the shadows, he returned to the hotel. He was saved having to brave the unwanted attention of the Night Porter by climbing up a builder's ladder that conveniently went past his second floor window. He cleaned himself up and waited to see what happened, certain that he was safe from any suspicion. Two days went by and Heath was preparing to move on

to pastures new and ladies green. Then Kathleen Evans, taking her dog for a walk on the lonely cliff top, was attracted to a rhododendron bushes by the sound of thousands of flies buzzing over something out of sight. When she got closer she could see a blackened leg sticking out from a pile of rags. The sight sickened her and sent her hurtling down the road to the nearest police station. When the police arrived they found the body as Heath had left it. They recovered Doreen's handbag and other belongings. Some way from the body they found a broken string of artificial pearls. A description of the woman was distributed and the Receptionist at the hotel instantly recognised her as the friend of Group Captain 'Brooke'. She showed the poster to the Group Captain and he expressed alarm at the fate of his newly found friend. The Receptionist suggested that he get in touch with the police immediately. He agreed. This time he didn't flit off to another locale and another identity. Instead, he went to the nearest police station to register his horror and disgust at the death of Miss Marshall. He told them that he had walked her part of the way home and then she had insisted that he returned to the hotel as it was getting so late. He cursed himself for not insisting on taking her all the way. While he was making his emotional statement, DC Sutern had been watching him closely. He left the room and looked at the photofit picture that had been recently circulated in respect of the Marjorie Gardner case. The likeness was good enough for the Detective to go back into the interview room and ask a straight question. 'Group Captain Brooke, is your real name Heath' Heath didn't turn a hair. He looked at the picture the DC showed him and admitted that it did look extraordinarily like him but insisted his name was Brooke and offered to go back to the hotel and get his RAF discharge papers that would back up his claim. Sutern wasn't satisfied and called in his Sergeant who suggested that the easiest way to settle the problem was to send to the hotel for 'Brooke's' luggage and settle the question there and then. There was nothing for Heath to do but sit and wait for the denouement. This he did calmly, chatting to the detectives and talking about the difficulties of settling back into civilian life.

An hour later DC Sutern was back at the station with Heath's few belongings packed in a sack. Heath watched with interest as they carefully searched through his bits and pieces and came up with a trio of interesting finds. One was the ticket for luggage left at Bournemouth Station. More incriminating was the return half of a first-class rail ticket issued to Doreen Marshall. Heath had a ready explanation. When he had been talking to the poor girl the evening before she died, she had mentioned that she had wanted to go to see some friends in Yeovil but only had a ticket valid for a straight journey to Waterloo. Neither of the policemen commented on this piece of specious information. As each damning piece of evidence was revealed Heath examined it with detached interest as if it had nothing to do with him. He was an intelligent man and must have known that he was in deep schtuk but he was perfectly relaxed and even made jokes about his situation. The clincher was a single artificial pearl found in the pocket of his suit. Heath considered for a moment. He was unaware at this point that the broken string of pearls had been found near the body of his victim. He started to explain that shortly before Doreen left she had shown him a broken string of pearls and asked if he knew anyone who could fix them. He had taken one of the pearls so that he could show it to a jeweller and get an estimate of the cost to repair it. Heath made the statement as if he didn't believe it either. With commendable restraint neither DC Sutern nor Inspector Spooner made any remark – just wrote the claim into their notebook. What the pearl was doing in Heath's pocket was never made clear. It could have been a macabre memento or it could possibly have worked its way into his pocket as he struggled with Doreen. Whatever – it was not something that could

be easily explained. Heath was taken to the railway station by DC Sutern and Inspector Spooner and his suitcase reclaimed from the Left Luggage depository. More incriminating and ultimately condemning evidence. In the suitcase was the riding crop that he had used on Marjorie Gardner.

The trial of Neville George Clevely Heath opened at the Old Bailey on 24th September 1946. The prosecution brought only the case of Marjorie Gardner before the Jury. They felt that bringing other charges might muddy the water. After all, it was a hanging crime and that could only be done once. The Crown had also guessed that Heath's defence was going to be insanity and if they brought up the murder of Doreen Marshall as well this might strengthen the feeling in the jurors mind that only someone with more than a tile loose could perform such barbarous acts on a woman's body. Heath didn't seem to care what happened. When asked by the Judge if he had any complaints, he stood and asked if he could possibly have his suspenders back as without them his socks wrinkled most unattractively over his ankles. On another occasion he asked if it would be possible to employ the services of a 'batman' to look after his clothes as the facilities in his cell were rather Spartan and he had no way of looking after his suit. This went down a bomb with His Lordship and didn't exactly endear him to the jury who, to a man, were ex-servicemen and for one reason or another relished the opportunity of sitting in judgment on the ex-Squadron Leader. Heath's defence lawyer brought in a psychologist who rather spoilt his case by splitting hairs. He told the jury that he had spent some time with the defendant and was willing to judge him 'morally insane'. Pushed for a definition he claimed that it was only possible to go on the evidence and that a man who had allegedly done the sort of things Heath had done *must* have a kink in the morals and therefore could not be said to be normal. A lot of time was spent on this question but in the end it could not be proved that at the time of his actions Heath could be deemed insane. The trial went ahead.

Heath was the only one who appeared to have no interest in what was going on. He lounged comfortably in his seat, occasionally yawning or smiling to anyone who caught his eye. He wasn't called to testify in his own defence and when he was offered a chance to express remorse before the jury went out to consider their verdict, he just considered the request, half smiled, looked at the jury and nodded. Not a good move. Sandbagged by the harrowing pictures and the intimate medical evidence that they had been forced to sit through they were in no mood to be lenient. It took them less than an hour to return a verdict of guilty. The judge, Mr Justice Morris, sentenced Heath to death by hanging. Heath nodded amiably, shook hands with his defending barrister and followed the warders from the dock. The jury's verdict had been unanimous and the judge's summing up left no hostages to fate which might have been the basis for an appeal. It mattered little. Heath had no intention of appealing. Now that he had been sentenced he just wanted to get the whole unsavoury affair over. His execution was set for the 16th October in Pentonville Prison. Heath slept most of the night then rose, washed and shaved, ate his breakfast, and carefully dressed. While he was waiting for the Governor and his entourage to arrive, the executioner, Albert Pierrepoint, asked if there was anything he would like. Heath asked for a whiskey and 'considering the circumstances you had better make that a double'. He walked calmly to the gallows and died without confessing to the murder. As a murderer, Neville Heath was undoubtedly unspeakable. But he died with style.

3
Peter Kürten - The Monster of Düsseldorf

I guess it is no coincidence that Germany produced some of the most horrific films of the early cinema. *M*, released in 1931 with a young Peter Lorre, still holds its own against anything made since. It is interesting that during the period when Peter Kürten was performing unspeakable horrors on the citizens of Düsseldorf, the great German director, Fritz Lang, was making *M*. It must be one of those eerie overlaps between fact and fiction that crop up with a greater frequency than is generally acknowledged. Kürten was the sort of bloke you wouldn't mind getting into your deserted carriage on the last underground train on a Saturday night. At the time of his rebirth as a murderer he was 48 years old, a little over 5ft 2ins, impeccably dressed and doused in cheap toilet water.

Kürten's early life wasn't easy. He was the runt of a pack of 13 born to a moulder and his wife in the largish village of Cologne-Mülheim. His father took a great delight in working out his frustrations on his wife and children. Peter was one of his father's favourites when it came to sexual abuse and the boy lost all sense of right and wrong. But he was intelligent and played the game. He believed that behind drawn curtains the scenes enacted in his home where the norm. Nobody talked about it because it was a family thing – something like going to the toilet or masturbating – everybody was into it but it wasn't mentioned in polite company. Although small of frame, Peter was strong beyond his years. He was only six when he had his first run-in with the authorities. Some of his older siblings had made a raft out of tree trunks and some old wooden crates. They kept it tethered to the banks of the Rhine with a long rope. Peter loved playing on it but soon just sitting and watching the water lap against the sides began to get boring. He was playing on the raft with a boy a little older than himself. The play turned into a scuffle. Peter lost his cool. He threw himself at his opponent, pushed him over the side and held his head under water. The boy managed to escape but Peter got a visit from the local constable which triggered another beating from his drunken father. By the time he was 13, the boundaries of normal behaviour were completely lost. A year later, his father was sent to prison for incest. With his father out of the way he had nothing to fear and his sadistic tendencies were let off the rein. He had become friendly with the local pest control officer, or as it was known in those far off, non-PC days, the ratcatcher. The job of ratcatcher does not call for great sensitivity. The only qualification is a proficiency in the art of killing animals. Peter was an apt pupil. The thing he loved most was to catch an animal alive and then torture it to death. Blood was what excited him most and he had an unerring instinct for being at the slaughter house or a local farm when there was any killing going on. The family moved to Düsseldorf and Peter was indentured as a moulder's apprentice.

The greater liberty presented by living in a city at first frightened then excited Kürten. With puberty came an even greater pressure for an emotional outlet. His early days had been made hellish by his father's sexual deprecations and the only solace he found was in the company of his sadistic ratcatcher friend. It was natural that his method of sexually satisfying his urges should emulate the only guidance he had been given by his father. He found a playmate. Gerda lived in the same street and was the only one not put off by the malevolent reputation the Kürten family brought with it. She was soon to regret this lack of selectivity when making friends. Gerda suggested a picnic. Peter didn't know what a picnic was but he was game for anything which would give him the exclusive company of his young friend. They walked the four miles to the Grafenberger Wald. Peter was on his best behaviour. Until they left the road and went into the wood. He grabbed the girl and started pawing at her clothes. At first Gerda struggled silently, not wanting to cause embarrassment by drawing attention to what was happening. The more she struggled, the more brutal Kürten became. He struck her across the face several times, releasing her screams. To stop her, he gripped her neck in his strong fingers and clamped his other hand over her mouth. Gerda was near death when someone who had heard her cries appeared. Like a startled animal Kürten sprung away from the girl and disappeared into the trees. Exhausted he found himself a hollow and dropped off to sleep. When he awoke it was dark. That suited him. He was afraid to return home, sure that the girl would have reported him to the police. He need not have worried. Shame kept Gerda from telling anyone what had happened. She knew that the only response would be that if she was stupid enough to go into the woods by herself with a young man of Kürten's character, she deserved all that she got. Kürten liked the woods. It reminded him of the days he had spent with his ratcatcher friend. He decided to live there until the imagined hue and cry had died down and he could return to his home. He supported himself by catching rabbits and birds and raiding nearby houses and farms.

Later he told the police that it was a wonderful time when he could think about himself. He could imagine causing horrendous accidents that would kill thousands of people and would make his name feared throughout the country. At last he had enough of his solitary existence and returned home. His father was now out of prison and back with the family. He was a changed man. The forced abstention from the booze during his prison sentence and a general breakdown in his health made him no match for his increasingly violent son. Kürten went about his daily quota of petty crime and sexual harassment as if he were invulnerable. It couldn't last. Picked up for petty theft and imprisoned, he spent his time in solitary confinement planning new scams and better methods of torture. One thing he saw clearly. To stand any chance of getting away with his crimes he must create a persona that didn't mark him down as a criminal on sight. Released from prison he went to the barber and had a regulation haircut and a close shave. That night he broke into a tailor's shop and selected a suitably conservative wardrobe topped off with a Fedora. His new image didn't alter his character. He became obsessed with fire and began torching houses and factories whenever the mood was on him. He loved the excitement of watching the often futile attempts of the fire fighters to quench the flames and the grief of the families as they watched their house razed to the ground. His luck ran out at last and he was arrested. He refused to confess to his crimes and was handed down what was hoped would be a short, punitive sentence of hard labour. He promised to join the Army and had part of his prison sentence suspended. His military career lasted exactly 24 hours. But deserting the military wasn't as easy as burning houses or molesting young girls. Within a few days the military police were knocking on his door and he was back in prison. It was more of the same. The sadistic military warders took a great delight in beating the undersized deserter. Peter withdrew further into himself, fantasising on what he would do to get even with his persecutors and the public at large once he had regained his freedom. He was released in April 1913. He re-established himself in the home of another convict he had met in prison. He hardly went out of the house for a month while the ravages of the prison regime faded and he could assume his gentle, conservative manner again. His forced inactivity gave him more chance to brood on the unfairness of the world. By the time he was ready to resume his nefarious activities, he had lived each sadistic moment of it in his mind. Now all he needed was a victim. He found her in the bedroom of a public house in Cologne-Mülheim. The daughter of the publican, 13-year-old Christine Klein slept by the open window of her ground floor room. It was a fatal mistake. Kürten's intention was to burgle the inn. When he found himself standing over the young girl he instantly forgot the robbery. She sensed his presence and opened her eyes. Before she could scream his hand closed over her throat and she was dragged roughly from her bed. As she struggled Kürten took out a sharp pocket knife and with a swift, practiced slash, slit her throat. As she fell, gagging on her own blood, he ripped off her nightdress and masturbated on her. It was what he had always dreamed it would be when he laid exhausted and in pain in his prison cell. At last, it was payback time.

Next day, Kürten returned to the pub. The excitement in the streets was gratifying. People were talking about him. But he was invisible, omnipotent. He joined the regulars in the bar and listened to and even embellished the speculation about the terrible crime that had been committed only a shudderingly delicious couple of yards away from where they sat. A bizarre incident that might have led a more diligent police force to look elsewhere, the only piece of real evidence was found at the scene: a white pocket handkerchief smelling of cologne. The investigating officers overlooked this aromatic clue, overwhelmed by the initials 'PK' embroidered in the corner. They arrested Christine's father – Peter Klein. The blood on the handkerchief confirmed his guilt as far as the police were concerned.

Kürten was no longer the tearaway of his formative years. Now he buried his true nature in his mild man of the people act. He even got married. His act was so good that even his wife was fooled. She saw

him as a quiet, undemonstrative husband, conservative and softly spoken.

It was 1925 and Germany was in the greatest depression that had ever befallen a civilised country. The 'wheel-barrow' economy was in full swing. Money meant nothing. Only items that could be held in the hand had value. But the mild-mannered Kürten seemed to be doing very well. Nobody, not even his wife, seemed to have any idea exactly what he did but whatever it was it kept him in suits and put meat on the table.

Kürten had served his apprenticeship as a budding serial killer. Killing wasn't enough for him. He needed a more lasting memento – wanted to feel bonded to his victims. The best way to do this was to drink their blood. Before long there was talk of a vampire on the prowl. It gave Kürten a kick to sit in a bar, quiet and unassuming, and listen to his legend being built on the lips of his companions. He had become a celebrity. The reading public waited impatiently for each new episode. And he didn't disappoint them. He even felt frustrated when, after an attack, it wasn't reported. Sometimes this was because the women attacked had been too ashamed or too frightened to report the assault. Sometimes it was not considered important enough. Then, early in 1929, he threw aside all restraint and went on a killing rampage. Using a long-bladed pair of tailor's scissors he stabbed several people in quick succession. After tearing out their throat in his trademark Vampire fashion he combined his love of fire with his bloodlust and set fire to the body.

A week later he came across Rudolf Sheer walking in the park. He followed at a distance until they reached a cluster of trees and overhanging branches. It was early evening and the path was in deep shadow. Kürten ran up behind Sheer and let the impetus of his body weight carry them into the bushes. Before his victim had time to recover Kürten stabbed him repeatedly with the scissors then sat beside the bleeding man and watched him die. The blood pumping thickly from the wounds was too

The mild-mannered Monster of Düsseldorf, Peter Kürten. (Popperfoto)

much to resist and he fell on the warm body and drank deeply. Kürten was now beyond any vestige of morality that might have remained after the lessons of his childhood. The papers were now full of his exploits and he felt obliged to provide the editors with a gruesome front page. He met a housemaid on her day off. She was taken in by his quiet manner and smart suit. He took her walking on the banks of the river and professed to being enchanted with her. She told the staff at the house where she worked that she had met a 'gentleman' and she thought that this might be the real thing. Kürten seemed to have been quite taken with her and tried to get past the ritual kissing and cuddling. She was 'not that sort of girl'. It wasn't enough for her swain. He suddenly produced his lethal scissors from his pocket and plunged them deep into the women's throat. He dragged her into a ditch and lapped up the blood spurting from a severed artery.

The police were now getting a lot of flak from terrified residents. It made them irritable and they were looking for someone to blame. Several men were arrested but released when they provided concrete alibis. Kürten decided it was time to move on. Most of the murders had been within a short distance of his lodgings and he felt that the bumbling police might stumble across him by accident. He took a room on the outskirts of Düsseldorf in the suburb of Flehe. It wasn't long before Kürten felt the urge to prowl again. At an agricultural show he spotted two young girls. He watched them from a discreet distance until he was certain that they were on their own. When they left the grounds he followed. On a quiet country lane he overtook them and stopped in front of them. The girls, Gertrude Haimacher (14) and her younger sister Louise (5), weren't frightened. It was a time before mothers warned children about talking to strangers and an adult was looked on as a source of security. Kürten searched through his pocket, mimed frustration and explained to the girls that he had forgotten to buy some cigarettes. Helpfully, Gertrude offered to go back to the show and

buy some for him. He thanked her and suggested she leave the little one with him so that she could run faster. Gertrude readily agreed. As soon as she left Kürten bundled the baby into the ditch at the side of the road and strangled her. In a frenzy he bit huge chunks of flesh from the little body. Gertrude returned with the cigarettes and was disturbed to find that the kind gentleman and her sister were no longer waiting for her. She didn't know what to do. As she hesitated, Kürten sprang from a place of concealment, grabbed her around the neck and pulled her into a small copse at the side of the road. She tried to scream but she was in the hands of an expert and could only gasp in silence. Kürten drew the wicked bladed scissors from the home-made sheath tucked under the waistband of his trousers and Gertrude's gasps were silenced for good. Kürten then sexually assaulted the body and hid it under some bushes. Tired, he went back to his solitary room and slept for a night and a day. He awoke refreshed, meticulously cleaned his suit and went out into the night. The bright lights of the agricultural show with its roundabouts and stalls attracted him once more. It was a place were he could merge in the crowd. A place to observe and choose. He was like a wolf sizing up a flock of sheep, deciding which were most vulnerable and easiest to take. Gertrude Shulte was another housemaid looking for a chance to kick over the traces. Kürten introduced himself and chatted about nothing in particular. He seemed to have a bit of cash to spare and she agreed to accompany him the following evening to the show. When she arrived at their rendezvous the next day, he was waiting. He suggested that, as it was such a lovely evening, instead of getting the bus they should walk. It wasn't what Gertrude had in mind but she didn't argue. On the walk Kürten brought up the subject that was occupying the front pages of the newspapers: the murder and assault of the two young girls. He theorised that the site of the murder must be somewhere near where they were walking and suggested that they enter the wood to see what they could see. Gertrude pretended

Kürten uses his trademark scissors to kill Gertrude Haimacher, aged 14.

to be shocked at the idea but the thought of a vicarious thrill at visiting the murder scene was too much to miss and she let Kürten persuade her. Once out of sight Kürten grabbed the woman and attempted to force himself on her. She was stronger then she appeared and was able to fight Kürten off. In a rage he whipped out his scissors and before she could run away, thrust the blade into her neck. She managed to stagger away, screaming through the thick blood pouring from the jagged wound in her throat. Beyond reason Kürten followed her, stabbing repeatedly at her body. Her screams saved her. A couple of men on their way to the show heard them and came to find out what was going on. Kürten wasn't looking for complications. He turned and ran. Although terribly wounded, Gertrude recovered and was able to furnish the police with a full description of her attacker.

The newspapers were full of the Monster of Düsseldorf. They ran stories about the growing cult of Satanism. Covens of witches were rumoured to have moved into the area. Several people came forward to claim that from the description of the fiend they were able to state it was a person known to them who had died recently. Detectives from Berlin were drafted in. They discounted the supernatural nature of the attacker. They posited a Sadism Club like the infamous Hellfire Club that had shocked England less than 50 years earlier. They had a theory but they were as luckless as the local police in substantiating it. Attacked by the newspapers for doing nothing to stop the killings, chastised by their superiors who wanted action, the desperate detectives decided to try shock tactics to unearth the criminal.

The body of Maria Hahn, one of Kürten's earlier victims, was still in the mortuary. It gave Detective Bloomfeld an idea. The generally accepted theory was that their quarry was a frequenter of beer kellers and music halls. Bloomfeld obtained a coffin and had a secret mechanism installed. He then laid Maria's body in the coffin and took it to one of the most popular kellers. The coffin was placed on a table in the centre of the room. He called for attention and then launched into a long, rambling speech about the killer in their midst. At the climax he threw open the coffin lid and Maria's body was jerked into a sitting position by the spring that had been installed. The macabre Jill-in-the-box caused pandemonium as the clientele decided they wanted to be somewhere else and stormed the exits. Bloomfeld had placed detectives at vantage points around the room. The idea was that when the evidence of his crime was sprung, literally, on him, the murderer's reaction would condemn him. The detectives were lucky not to be crushed by the stampede and it was decided that the experiment had not been a good idea.

Kürten loved the theatricality of the failed attempt to catch him. He was back in the limelight with a vengeance. The public couldn't get enough of the macabre entertainment. In spite of the country being in the very depths of depression, newspaper sales went through the roof. In September Kürten lost the use of the scissors that had served him so faithfully. In a determined attack on a flower-seller, he had the misfortune to break off the blade of his trusty weapon when it struck bone. He still managed to finish off his victim and feed on her blood but it was the end of his calling-card weapon. Sad though he was to have to resort to some other method, he didn't moon over it. He found a suitably heavy ball-pane hammer, left in his lodgings by a former tenant, and took to the streets to try it out. It suited his purpose admirably. Three servant girls fell victim to Kürten and his ball-pane hammer in quick succession. But Kürten wasn't happy with his new weapon of destruction. Although there was blood, it seeped rather than gushed. It wasn't what Kürten wanted or needed. So he bought another pair of scissors. The police were now, since the evidence of the broken blade, looking for a tailor with an urge to cut up more than serge. But they overlooked the possibility that robbed of his favourite weapon the killer would acquire another. It was a sad oversight. Kürten tried out his new weapon on a five-year-old girl. He thrust his dreaded blade into her tiny body an estimated 40 times. The small body was so mutilated that the coroner was unable to say if any other offence had been visited on the poor child.

Peter Kürten had now completely skipped the bounds of humanity or reasonable behaviour but it was an uncharacteristic act that brought about his downfall and arrest. Maria Budlick was another domestic. She had just lost her job and was about to catch a train to return to Cologne where her parents lived, when she met Kürten. She told him her problem and he offered to help. He dissuaded her from catching the train and promised to get her some lodgings that would tide her over until he arranged for her to take up her new job. Kürten bought her a meal and suggested he accompanied her to the hostel where she could sleep for the night. The road passed through a secluded wood. Maria was feeling a little apprehensive. Kürten had broached one of his favourite subjects as they walked – The Monster of Düsseldorf. Maria had read about it, who hadn't, in the newspapers and it was one of the favourite subjects below stairs. She was happy to have an escort who was solicitous and showed no fear of the dark, overhanging trees. She was relieved when they were clear of the menacing woods and when Kürten told her that they were close to where he lived and suggested that they call in for a drink before going on to the hostel, she agreed. At his flat Kürten was a model of propriety. He cooked Maria an omelette and sat and drank a cup of coffee with her before catching a tram across town to the hostel. At least, that was where he told her they were going. Where he was taking her was to the site of his first crime – the Grafenberger Wald. Maria was still not worried. Kürten suddenly turned to her and in a low, menacing voice told her that she was in a wood where there was nobody else for miles and she could scream as much as she liked and nobody would hear her. With that he dropped his false friendliness and threw her to the ground. She fought hard but it was a one-sided struggle that was bound to go Kürten's way. Just when she was about to go under Kürten relaxed and sat up. He sat and stared at her for a

long time. She was afraid to move, frightened that any movement might excite Kürten into renewing his attack. Gruffly he asked her if she remembered where he lived. In spite of being terrified she still had her wits about her and told him that she had no idea. He thought about it, stood up and towered over her, warned her that it would be the worse for her if she went to the police. Then, inexplicably, he turned and walked away.

Maria was an intelligent girl, in spite of letting herself be talked into danger by Kürten; when she recovered her composure she went to the police. She led them to Kürten's flat but Kürten was out. As they left he spotted them and decided that it was not healthy to return there. He spent the night wandering the streets of Düsseldorf. What thoughts went through his head can only be imagined. It was obvious that he was subject to some sort of trauma. What else would explain the uncharacteristic release of the woman he had taken to the scene of his former crime? It must have been a field day for Freud trying to work out Kürten's motivation. Not the motivation for committing his horrendous crimes but the reason for his sudden change of heart. Early the next morning Kürten sent a message to his wife to meet him at a nearby cafe. Over coffee he catalogued his crimes. She had never suspected that her husband was anything but what he had seemed. True, he did spent quite a lot of time away from home but he had explained this was to do with his business and she had accepted it without reservation. Horrified and not a little frightened she agreed to go to the police and inform on him. He explained to her that before she told them his story she must make sure that she would receive the reward promised for information leading to his arrest. His wife hurried thankfully away to do his bidding and Kürten ordered another coffee and a meat plate and waited calmly for the police.

When Peter Kürten's trial began on the 13 April 1931, the police were out in force to hold back the crowds surrounding the courthouse. To try to relieve the pressure, some of the chambers and passageways were decked out with exhibitions of weapons, clothes and even bones that had a connection with the trial taking place in the court room a few yards away.

Now that he had been captured, on his own terms, Kürten revelled in his notoriety. He was at last able to acknowledge the fame that was his. Psychologists queued up to get a chance of questioning him. Each with his own theory about what had turned the polite, mild-mannered man into the bestial monster he had become. What soon became evident was that he was highly intelligent with an amazing memory. Happy to co-operate, he was able to fill in details of crimes that had baffled the police for years. He claimed that there was nothing selective in his crimes. He just killed anyone that was unfortunate enough to cross his path. The jury took nine days to reach the verdict of guilty, nine times! Guilty for each of the murders for which he had been tried. The execution was set for the 1 July 1931 – death by decapitation in the courtyard of the Kingelputz Prison in Cologne. While he waited for the dignitaries to settle in their places, he chatted amicably to the executioner. He wanted to know if he had been present at many beheadings, the man said he had. Kürten asked him a question that had been bothering him ever since he was sentenced to death, 'Do you think that after you have cut off my head I will be able to still think – even for a few seconds? I'd love to hear the blood gushing from the stump of my neck. It would be the pleasure of all pleasures.' The executioner couldn't believe his ears and reported the conversation to the Governor and suggested that Kürten was mad. That avenue had been explored to the point of boredom at the hearing and mad or not Kürten, the Monster of Düsseldorf got the chop.

4
Belle Gunness

Belle was the sort of woman on which America was proud to be built. Strong mentally and physically, it was easy to imagine her, knelt behind a wagon wheel, firing a Winchester at the encircling Indians, praising God with her dying breath. When she wasn't doing that or baking apple pie, she would be out in the fields dragging the one-bladed plough over the rock-strewn ground to sow the winter corn. She looked like, and was, a daughter of the soil. One of the huddled masses that had left Europe to find a new life and intended to have it – whatever hardships must be overcome. She was born in 1859 in Norway. Her father was a magician, a travelling illusionist. Belle spent her formative years travelling around the country, often cold and hungry, always overworked by her overbearing father. When she wasn't looking after her father, she doubled as a diminutive shiel outside the magic tent. At six, she was an accomplished juggler and tightrope walker. As she grew older and her father's skill with legerdemain began to fail, she was reduced to earning a little extra money doing favours for men more interested in her lithe athletic body than her juggling skills. By the time she was 24, she had secreted away a tidy little nest egg. A few years earlier her sister had emigrated to the USA with a trapeze artist she met at one of the circuses. She was happy to get away from the domination of her father and frequently urged Belle to do the same. She was so persuasive that when Belle's father conveniently died, she had already made arrangements to join her sister in Chicago.

Belle was a quarter of a century too late to be a pioneering wife but she was just as determined to stake her claim to the land as any homesteader.

America in the 1880s was still a developing country. The only difference between America and the scores of countries around the world that were also claiming to be 'developing' was that the Union had the basic commodities and skills that made its emergence as a frontline nation only a matter of time. It was the era of vast social engineering and entrepreneurial adventure. Within months of shuffling through the pens of Ellis Island, she was married. Her husband was a Swede, Albert Sorensen, who had already got a grip on the American Dream. He had started working 16-hour days building railways. Before long, he was supplying the workers with groceries and cooked meals. When the railway teams moved on he stayed put and opened a store in Chicago. It was just what Belle was looking for – a ready-made base on which to build her fortune. Working side by side, they steadily built up the business until they were earning a comfortable living. Albert wanted children but it was not on Belle's menu. A compromise was fashioned and the couple adopted three teenage girls. A convenient work force that Belle could control. It still wasn't enough for Belle but Albert was tired and wanted to rest on his moneybags. As the new century was born, Sorensen died. Belle expressed grief but didn't appear to be exactly grief-stricken. It may have been because Albert was heavily insured for $10,000, a fortune at that time.

Belle's sudden good fortune did not sit well with her late husband's relatives and they claimed that it was not a heart attack that had killed Sorensen but a huge dollop of arsenic fed to him by his less than grieving widow. They kicked up so much fuss that a coroner's hearing was announced. Albert's body was to be exhumed and the results filtered through the court and on to the police blotter. The family relaxed and waited for their suspicions to be proven and Albert's fortune to head their way. Belle was not into relaxation. She was now a woman of substance. Diligently she worked on all concerned in the investigation of her late husband's death and convinced them that it was a waste of time and taxpayers' money to investigate further.

When things quietened down Belle bought a confectionery shop. It soon became obvious that the shop was to money what quicksand is to a careless horseman and she watched her hard-earned *valuta* dribble away. Not for long! Once convinced of the lemon she was sucking, Belle put Plan A into operation and insured the business for three times what it was worth (if a failing business can have a value) and waited for a suitable moment. It had been a hot summer and the clapboard building was tinder dry. Belle waited until the dead of night when there was a breeze blowing through the streets and set fire to the building. She stayed in her room above the store until the downstairs was well alight and a neighbour had called out the firemen. She was always good with an audience and when there were enough witnesses present, she staggered out of the shop and collapsed dramatically in front of them. Next morning she was told that her store had been gutted.

The assessors of the insurance company were not pleased. It was only a couple of weeks since they had talked the grieving widow into taking out a far greater policy than she had originally wanted. They felt badly used and refused to pay out, using the small print to justify their lack of generosity. Belle was ready for that. She had also read the small print and was more than willing to take them through the courts. But instead she preferred a quicker and more effective ploy. She talked to a journalist and told him what the insurance company were up to. He agreed to run with the story but needed evidence to corroborate her claims. Belle professed herself happy to oblige. She went straight to her insurers and told them that if they didn't pay up, they would see the story emblazoned all over the *Chicago Times*. And she had the letters from the journalist to prove it. They settled immediately.

Belle guessed that she had outlived her welcome in Chicago and moved to Indiana. She decided that she wanted to put her money into something that offered security. The bank suggested a property on the outskirts of town. It was cultivated and had all the appurtenances of a modern farm. Belle went to look at it and decided it was just what she was looking for. The opposite of what her peripatetic life had been before she emigrated to the land of opportunity. Impatiently, Belle waited for the sale to be finalised and then moved in. Belle set the girls on cleaning the house from top to bottom while she did a tour of the farm with the handyman she had inherited. A couple of days later a neighbour, a fellow Norwegian, came a-calling – Peter Gunness. Belle fired her hired hand and married Gunness. She had expected him to be as enthusiastic about making the farm work as she was herself but all she got from the union was an unwanted baby – a son, Philip. Belle wanted to get rid of her husband but he was happy where he was. He didn't want to go back to working for a boss and making his own breakfast. It was time to act. Belle, with her brand new name of Gunness, called on the local insurance company. They thought their Christmas had come early when she told them that she wanted to insure not only the farm but also her three girls, Myrtle, Lucy and Jennie, her baby son Philip and, of course, herself and her husband. Two months later Peter Gunness was the victim of a freak accident. While working in the farm slaughterhouse a little distance from the house, a meat cleaver developed a mind of its own, leapt from a shelf and cleaved Peter's head in twain. Belle put up such a great act as a distraught widow that the local Sheriff accepted her account of what had happened and the insurance company paid up without question. But there were those in the town, relatives and friends of Gunness, who were not happy with the outcome and called for an inquiry. They pointed out that it was almost impossible for anyone to put the cleaver on the shelf that it had presumably fallen from without a ladder. And why would anyone go to all that trouble to place a frequently used implement out of easy reach? The local doctor took another look at the injury and opined that the weight alone of the falling chopper was not enough to inflict the terrible injuries that occurred. Belle stayed out of the furore. Unfortunately, this wasn't the case with Jennie, the eldest of Belle's adopted children. She told anyone that would listen that her mother had killed her father. This was taken as enough evidence to warrant a Coroner's Court. Jennie was the star witness but she refused to twinkle. Asked to repeat her allegation, she refused and denied ever saying anything about her father's death. Belle was called to give evidence and put on such a bravura performance that there was not a dry eye in the court when the coroner dismissed her. Without the testimony of Jennie there was nothing to go on and the case was dropped.

Although Belle was as fit as any man, she still needed another pair of strong hands to work the farm. The girls were fine on the lighter jobs but as they grew older they were becoming more independent and troublesome. She took on a stranger

to the district, Ray Lamphere. His surly manner suited Belle. It ensured that he wouldn't get on familiar terms with the easy-going locals. Only Jennie was giving her cause for concern. Although the girl had been intimidated into withdrawing her statement in the court, she still knew what she knew and was holding it like a Damoclean sword over Belle's head. A dangerous thing to do. Belle offered Jennie a way out. She promised to send her away to a boarding school in California. Jennie jumped at the chance of escape. Belle waited until it was an accepted fact that Jennie would be leaving then enticed her out to the barn where she had disposed of her worthless husband and used the cleaver on Jennie. Working swiftly she dismembered the body and put the pieces into the big, high pressure boiler in which she prepared the pig swill. To all enquiries Belle answered that Jennie was alive and well and living in Los Angeles.

Belle had by this time become disenchanted with her life as a daughter of the soil. It was back-breaking work and the profit was minimal. There would never be enough money for her to retire into the comfortable life that she had thought she was buying with the farm. She decided to use what she had got as bait. Posing as a wealthy widow, she inserted an advertisement into a Chicago newspaper asking for a similarly well-breached gentleman to join fortunes with her. She stipulated that any gentleman not willing to follow up an introductory letter with a personal visit might as well save the stamp. It was a tempting offer and there was no lack of hopeful suitors willing to make the trip to Indiana. They arrived at the farm, pockets bulging, sheaves of paper proving they were men of substance and just the person for whom the wealthy widow was looking. Mr Moo was so insistent that he was for her that he promised to pay off the mortgage on Belle's farm. And he had brought the money to prove it. Belle played the reluctance card and he pushed her to

Belle Gunness wields her axe to bloody effect.

accept his offer. Belle waited for a time when he wouldn't be missed for a few days, took him to the killing sheds and used her efficiency with the axe to increase her fortune. She took a chance and called Lamphere to help her dispose of the body. He took it all in his stride and pocketed the bundle of dollar bills she gave him without thanks. Next up was George Anderson. A farmer, recently widowed, he was looking for someone with similar interests to share his life. He wasn't taken with Belle. The years of drudgery on the farm had thickened her figure and hardened her face. It wasn't what he was looking for to replace his late wife. And he hadn't brought his money with him. Belle was not happy about that but decided that she should give him the full treatment and hope to persuade him to return to his home in Missouri, sell up his farm and hurry back to her with his bags stuffed with cash. Pampered, George began to wonder if maybe it wouldn't be a bad idea to move in. They discussed her mortgage and he agreed to pay it if they married. They drank a toast and retired to bed. In the early morning he awoke to find Belle leaning over him with a lamp in her hand. Her face was so menacing that George let out a scream and leapt from his bed. Without a word Belle turned and hurried from the room. That was enough for George Anderson. He dressed, collected his belongings and set out on foot for the station. Belle watched him leave from her bedroom window. Anderson caught the next train out and Belle never heard from him again.

This minor setback didn't bother Belle. In fact, she had so many replies it was a matter of selection. Ole Budsburg from Wisconsin looked like a good catch. He told her in his introductory letter that he was 62, recently widowed and a retired school teacher. He said he wasn't too bothered about the physical side of the relationship. He had no other family but a son in the navy and he hadn't seen him for over 10 years. He was quite willing to use his financial resources to clear her mortgage in exchange for a comfortable home. Belle was willing and he appeared a few weeks later with his life's savings in his pocket. Belle wasted no time on him. Once she had his money in her hand she suggested a tour of the farm and led him to the slaughterhouse. She called in Lamphere to clear up and went to bed. She was getting a little worried about the collection of human bones that was piling up. The boiler was great for rendering the bodies unrecognisable but it didn't destroy the bone. Lamphere suggested that they buried the bodies in the pig pens. It would save them having to dismember them and the smell from the pigs would hide the stench from the decomposing bodies. Belle agreed that it was a good solution to their problem. She was still getting answers to her advertisement but the letter that made the most impression was from an Oscar Budsburg, Ole's sea-faring son. He had unexpectedly turned up at his father's home to find his mother dead, his father gone and the house sold. From the headmaster of his father's old school he discovered that his father had left to get married. The forwarding address was Mrs Belle Gunness. Belle didn't know what to do. She didn't think that Philip, the only one of her children still living at home, would have noticed Ole. He had arrived late and been safely interred by the following morning, so she wrote a letter back to Oscar claiming that, although she had expected his father to visit her, he had never arrived. This seemed to satisfy Oscar Budsburg and he presumably returned to sea without investigating the disappearance of his father further. This was not to be the case when another of Belle's suitors came to call.

Belle had been having what could only be described as a fulsome correspondence with a farmer, Andrew Hegelein, from South Dakota. Before long Belle was writing the sort of letters that young girls write to the school stud and then are too embarrassed to post. She waffled on about how sweet he was and how much the children were looking forward to his arrival. Her letters were masterpieces and before he knew what had hit him, Andrew Hegelein was convinced that they were heaven meant for each other and he was on a train heading north, his entire fortune of $3000 tucked safely in his valise. Belle greeted him with loving arms, fed him a huge meal and took him to her bed. Hegelein, a bachelor, suddenly realised what he had been missing all those years. A couple of days of high-class servicing and the farmer from Dakota was putty in the hands of the experienced matron from Norway. When she suggested putting his money in her bank account 'for safety', he was happy to go with her to the bank and smile happily at what he saw as the start of a new life. Now that Belle had the money she was anxious to get rid of him. Again, the slaughterhouse was pressed into service. This time Lamphere was there at the death. While he distracted Hegelein's attention, Belle got the axe and struck. Lamphere had dug the hole good and deep in the pig sty and it was a matter of minutes to throw the body in and back-fill the earth.

Now Belle began to get problems from an unexpected quarter. Ray Lamphere, who had so far been her staunch ally, became jealous. Living with her on the lonely farm, her only confidant, he had fallen in love with her. He became resentful of the stream of men that passed through Belle's door and frequently her bed. He began to hang around when she had visitors and make snide remarks. After a particularly ferocious row, she sacked him. Aware that he was a source of extreme danger, Belle went to the Sheriff and complained that Lamphere was insane. She told them that she had put up with him for a long time because she felt sorry for him but now he had become so deranged and said such unbelievable things that she was forced to let him go. She explained that she felt it was her civic duty to warn the authorities of the possible danger to the general public. Her pleas were so convincing that Lamphere was picked up and examined by a doctor. The medical man had little experience of insanity and declared that, as far as he could tell, Lamphere, although deficient in social skills, was perfectly sane. Lamphere was released. He hadn't turned her in as she feared but Belle still wanted him permanently sidelined. A few days after Lamphere's release Belle was back at the Sheriff's office complaining that she feared for her safety. Lamphere had returned to the farm and threatened her. The Sheriff picked him up again and warned him off. By now Lamphere was not amused by the treatment meted out by his ex-employer and started dropping dark hints to anyone who would listen that there were things going on at the farm that would turn anyone's hair white overnight if they knew about them. But Belle's efforts to discredit him had worked and nobody was inclined to believe at what he hinted. Besides, it was so bizarre that it was patently the workings of a diseased mind.

Belle had managed to sideline Lamphere but her ability to control her immediate environment didn't extend to the outside world. A new cause for anxiety arrived in the post. Axel Hegelein, the departed Andrew's younger brother, had become worried. Since his brother had left home, nothing had been heard of him. Belle stuck to the plan that had been successful in the past and replied that Andrew had been there but they hadn't hit it off and he had left. He had mentioned that he was thinking of returning to Norway to visit the family home. Axel didn't buy that. He told her that he was coming to see her and find out exactly what had happened to his brother. Belle used the tactic that she had used before to divert suspicion. She went to a lawyer and made a big fuss about the danger she was in. She told him that she had always been terrified of Lamphere and that in spite of all the warnings he was still threatening her. He had promised to kill her and burn down the farm unless she took him back. She also hinted that she thought that Lamphere might have robbed some of the men who had come to see her. She seemed to be setting the scene so that when Axel Hegelein arrived she could point the finger at her ex-employee. Whatever her motivation there was no reason for anyone interested in the goings-on at the farm to investigate. Belle had taken on a new farm hand who lived in one of the outbuildings attached to the main house, Joe Moxan. He woke up in the middle of the night to find his room full of smoke. When he opened the door flames from the house prevented him leaving. He slammed the door, ran to the window and leapt out. He yelled at the top of his voice for Belle to get out but the house was completely enveloped in flame. Moxan sped off to the village and returned with helpers and the hand-pump fire engine. They were too late. As they arrived the house collapsed, the timber framed building was soon reduced to a heap of charcoal. The firemen poured water on the smoking ruins but it was just for show. Nobody and nothing could survive the inferno. When the embers had cooled off the search of the ruins turned up the remains of a headless female corpse and a young boy. Lying beside the corpse was a set of false teeth that were later identified as belonging to Belle. The doctor examined the body and made a startling announcement. The headless corpse was *not* that of Belle Gunness. It was an amazing statement considering that the body had been at the very centre of the fire and the heat must have melted much of the flesh from the body. Then a youth turned up at the Sheriff's office. He claimed to have been near the farm about the time that the conflagration started and saw Ray Lamphere run from the buildings. He was reluctant to say what he had been doing at the farm late at night but finally confessed that he was with a woman. This threw a new light on the matter. If the youth could put Lamphere on the spot, what did that do to the

physical evidence that pointed towards the body found at the farm not being that of Mrs Gunness? Belle's dressmaker was called in and came up with some measurements. They were a few years old, dating from the time when she had first arrived at the farm but the difference in size did seem to indicate that the body must be of some unknown person. Into the nicely brewing mystery came Axel Hegelein looking for his brother. Pressured to do something the Sheriff arrested Lamphere. Lamphere denied everything at first. He said that he had been nowhere near the property since he had been dismissed. It was too much for the local Sheriff and he passed the case on to higher authorities. Soon the place was buzzing with investigators from the police department and the insurance company. Belle, as always, had been heavily insured, although in this case there was nobody to benefit from the fire. By now she had been linked with her former life in Chicago and the circumstances of her first husband's death, and the suspicious fire that had befallen her confectionery shop were brought into the equation. Lamphere, in an effort to clear himself, confessed that he was aware that Belle lured men to the farm and then killed them for their money. He even confessed to helping her hide the evidence of her crime. He had done so, he claimed, because he was in mortal fear of his employer. Helpfully, he took the investigators to the farm and pointed out the sites of the hasty burials. One by one the bodies were unearthed and told a grisly tale of multiple murder most foul. In spite of the difference in size of the headless body, the evidence pointed to Lamphere and the police charged him with murder. Lamphere, faced with the possibility of the death penalty, changed his story. He claimed that he had been at the farm on the night of the fire but at the request of his ex-employer who told him she was in trouble and needed his help. She promised to pay him handsomely for his night's work and he decided to go and see what she wanted. When he arrived at the house, Belle had already killed and decapitated the woman. She was a someone that Belle had lured to the house on the pretext of needing a housekeeper. Belle had told Lamphere that she needed to disappear. When he protested and refused to help, she warned him that if she were taken she would tell the authorities that it was he that had committed the murders and that she had only recently, since he left the farm, become aware that anything untoward had been going on. Afraid that Belle might be able to carry off what she threatened, he had helped to torch the house. Belle had agreed to meet him later but had taken off across the fields and disappeared. It covered most of the salient points of the baffling case but it was difficult to see how the remarkable-looking woman could have got clean away without someone recognising her. And there was also the money found in Lamphere's lodgings. He tried to explain this away by claiming it was his savings but it didn't take a mathematician to work out that it was an impossibility on the sort of money he earned. The problem was that his later desperate statements contradicted those he had made earlier and in some cases revealed evidence that he was in possession of facts of which, if his later statements were true, he could not possibly have been aware.

At his trial Lamphere confessed to arson but denied any suggestion that he had a hand in the murders. He was sentenced to 20 years in the State Penitentiary and died a year later of consumption. Once the trial was over the speculation began. Opinion was divided. In spite of the findings of the trial, the favourite version of events was that Belle had lured the succession of wealthy men to the farm with the sole intent of robbing them and then disposing of the bodies. When Hegelein began making inquiries about the disappearance of his brother, she had decided that the time to do a neat vanishing trick had arrived. She had lured a woman to the house, killed and decapitated her. Then she had cold-bloodedly suffocated her son, laid her false teeth beside the woman's body that she had decapitated, set fire to her house and disappeared. The fact that there was little money in her bank account proved that she had kept the bulk of the stolen money, as much as $250,000 in some estimates, in the house and had disappeared with this leaving Lamphere to take the rap.

The scenario favoured by the authorities put Lamphere as the villain of the piece. Belle had invited various men to her house in a genuine attempt to find a soul mate. Her advertisement promised more than she had to offer. Her wannabe suitors arrived expecting a wealthy, cultured woman and were not happy to find a grossly overweight hog-farmer. They had all decided that they should leave for one reason or another, some promising to return with enough money to pay off the mortgage on the rapidly declining farm, others to clear up unfinished business. Unknown to Belle, Lamphere had lain in wait for them, murdered and robbed them and, under the pretence of working on the pig-pens, buried the bodies. When Belle became suspicious and threatened to inform the police, he had killed her and her son, cut off her head to confuse the investigators and add substance to the story he intended to tell to cover his tracks, and lay the blame for the murders that would inevitably be discovered on to the vanished Belle. He was amazed when the investigators lent credence to his story by declaring that the body was not that of Belle Gunness but of a taller, slighter women. Whatever might be the rights and wrongs of the case, it was Belle that got the starring role in common folklore. Rivalling the song about that other lady proficient with an axe, Lizzie Borden, 'You can't chop your mother up in Massachussets' – Belle had a ditty of her own.

Belle Gunness lived in Indiana, she always, always had a man
Ten, at least, went in her door, and never, never seen no more
Now all these men were Norska folk who came to Belle from Minnesote
They liked their coffee and their gin, they got it, plus a Mickey Finn
And now with cleaver poised so sure, Belle neatly cut their jugular
She put them in a bath of lime, and left them there for quite some time
There's red upon the Hoosier moon for Belle was strong and full of doom
Just think of all them Norska men who'll never see St Paul again

If it doesn't scan, fiddle about with the end syllables on some of the clines. Recently, an American TV company made a documentary based on the evidence presented at the trial of Lamphere as well as following up reported sightings of Belle in various cities throughout America. The last reported sighting was in Mississippi in 1931. Someone describing herself as a 'childhood friend' phoned the Sheriff's office and said that Belle was living in a great house and was a well-known figure in the neighbourhood. The informant failed to say exactly which neighbourhood or what name she was now living under. Neither did she leave her own name. Belle would have been 72 years old at this point and maybe her childhood friend, who presumably was about the same age, could have been mistaken.

If Belle did pull off the disappearing trick, it was a stunt that would have made her dear old magician daddy proud.

5
Edward Gein

If you were pitching Edward Gein's murderous story to a Hollywood producer, you would probably say that it's a cross between *Silence of the Lamb* and *Psycho*. The story that is about to be told is almost unbelievable but it is all true. So turn up the lights, make sure the telephone is handy and run your gig-lamps over this.

Edward's schooling had been rudimentary to say the least. He lived in a dirt-bowl farm in the centre of the Wisconsin plains. The local school house was over 10 miles away and there was no transport, public or private, to get there. For a while, Edward and his younger brother Henry bummed lifts from the parents of other boys in the outback but these were erratic and after a while the unfortunate children were just forgotten. The school authorities couldn't be bothered with making special arrangements for a couple of farm kids who were destined to become small-time farmers anyway. Occasionally someone would stir the pot and Edward and Henry would appear for a few days in the classroom but the lustre would go off the new-found zeal and when they subsequently didn't appear, they were marked as absent and forgotten again. When Edward did appear at school, it was remarked by his teachers that he was below average size, skinny, bright but incredibly shy, especially where women were concerned. Female teachers found it almost impossible to get him to look at them and, if he was forced to speak, he was desperately nervous and stammered uncontrollably. This made him the victim of every bully in the school. But he took the bullying like everything else – in silence. The farm was run by his mother. His father had gone off to seek work elsewhere and forgotten to return. This desertion hadn't improved his mother's disposition and she frequently warned her sons of the iniquities of the outside world – especially where the opposite sex was concerned. Although practically illiterate, Edward was interested in everything. When he could get away from the work with which his mother kept him supplied, he would go off and study nature. He had an extensive collection of birds' eggs and would bring home dead animals that he had found or killed and try to preserve them. Henry was happy with just not having to go to school but Edward rather resented the fact that he wasn't able to read books without a great deal of effort.

Then Mrs Gein died. One minute she was busy feeding the Rhode Island Reds and the next she was dead. Just like that. Edward found her. He carried her body into the house and sat and looked at it until Henry returned from working in the fields. Henry offered to go into town and get a doctor. Edward wouldn't have that. Anyway, it was too late. He made Henry help him carry the body into the kitchen and lay it on the table. Henry wasn't happy handling the body and when his brother started to undress his mother, he freaked out and ran off. Edward sat by the body of his mother for a long time. Then he went to the sink, pumped up a pail of water, got some soap and meticulously washed the body. When Henry returned Edward had dressed the body of his mother in a night dress and carefully combed her hair. He forced Henry to help him carry her up stairs and put her to bed. For five days he spent most of his time with the body of his mother. He washed her several times a day and changed her clothes whenever the fancy took him. Henry wasn't happy and kept telling Edward that they must inform the authorities that their mother was dead or they would get into trouble. On the fifth day, Edward washed the body again and dressed it in their mother's Sunday best. Happy that she was looking as good as a five-day-old corpse could look, he told Henry to go and get the undertaker. The funeral took place in the cemetery in town. It was the first time Edward had visited a cemetery. After the funeral he wandered through the tombstones laboriously picking out the inscriptions. He talked for a long time to the grave digger, an old alcoholic called Gus, and was clearly fascinated by some of the macabre stories the old man told. Soon he was going back whenever he could spare the time to hear more tall tales. Sometimes, when there was a body in the little hut that served as the administration centre and chapel for unwanted cadavers waiting a pauper's burial, his new friend would let him take a look at the body. They sometimes even stripped it and used the body as a subject for lewd and fanciful sexual experiments. It was one of the happiest times of Edward's miserable life. Edward pressed his hard won but decidedly rudimentary skills, into reading everything he could about human anatomy. In magazines he found advertisements for books dealing with the 'Scientific Facts of the Human Anatomy that every adult should know'. These were quasi-medical books that got around the laws dealing with pornography at that time and could still give the reader a vicarious thrill, safe in the knowledge that what he was reading was 'scientifically sound'. While Edward was away from the farm, a fire broke out in a nearby wood. It had been a long and exceptionally dry summer. Henry was afraid that the fire would spread to the fields and even to the house. He went and tried to stop the spread. The wind got up and he became trapped. Next day, when Edward found him he was dead and badly burned. Edward was inconsolable. In rapid succession he had lost the only two people he had in the world. After the funeral, he spent the night in the cemetery. There were several new graves and he spent a lot of time examining them.

There was little to do on the farm. It had been taken into a government scheme which made it more profitable to leave the land fallow than actually to produce something on it. With time hanging heavily on his hands, Edward returned to his pal Gus with a suggestion. He told him he was doing some experiments and he would need a body. Gus didn't ask what experiments he was doing but agreed that the next time he had a female body in he would get in touch. It was sooner than Edward had expected. Two days later Gus came out to the farm and told him he had the body of a 34-year-old woman who had died giving birth. Edward was enthusiastic and that night he accompanied Gus to the cemetery and while the old man kept watch, he dug up the body, put it on a cart he had brought for the job and pulled it back to the farm.

Edward's main interest was in the female sexual organs. He cut off the parts of the woman's body that he found interesting and fed the uninteresting bits to the hogs. The bits he kept, he stored in a shed. He used the same processes he had used to preserve the skins of animals he had shot or caught. The smaller pieces he kept in preserving jars using salt, diluted fertiliser or formaldehyde. He wasn't happy with the way the body, in spite of his efforts, persisted in decomposing. So he went back to Gus and got another body. Right from the start, he discovered that by carefully removing the skin, stretching it, rubbing it with rock salt and then carefully drying it, he could preserve it in mint condition. He got so proficient with it that he made himself articles of clothing out of the skins and would wear them around the house next to his skin. He wasn't really interested in men's bodies but took everything that Gus could send him. He particularly liked fondling the female sex organs and would walk around with a trophy in his pocket, caressing and even talking to it. He had only Gus to talk to and the old man, now that Edward was constantly paying him for his supplies of female corpses, was habitually drunk and unable to look after himself. Edward's largesse worked against him. Gus could no longer be relied on to do his job so he was packed off to an institution where he would be out of the way of temptation. That did not suit Edward but there was nothing he could do about it. Anyway, he'd had enough of 'working' on stinking cadavers. For a while he just 'experimented' with the bits of body he had already acquired. Gradually, his constant handling and the process of decay robbed him of his gruesome toys. The thought of returning to the cemetery and the hard work in liberating new bodies from the graves did not appeal. Besides that the bodies he had worked on so far had either been old, in the ground for too long or were in some way imperfect. What he wanted was something fresh. Something that he could preserve and 'study'.

His first victim ran the saloon. She was a big-busted woman and the diminutive Edward had always had fantasies about her. For her part, whenever their paths crossed, she treated him as if he were an imbecile. He had always taken her jokes diffidently but they rankled. He sat in the corner and watched her all evening. He had no problem about killing her. Watching her moving around, joking and laughing was an extra bonus. He knew that shortly all that flesh would be his – and it would be quiet and pliant and he would be able to do what he liked with it without complaint. When the last customer left he got up and walked over to the bar. Mary was surprised to see him. She hadn't noticed him in the shadows. She told him she was closing up and he had better leave. He just walked around the bar, pulled a pistol from his pocket and shot her in the head. It was all over so fast that she hit the floor with the glass she was wiping still in her hand. Edward quickly turned out the lights and closed the shutters. He sat at the window watching the deserted street until he was satisfied that there was nobody about that was likely to spring an unpleasant surprise on him. When he decided that the local inhabitants were safely tucked up in bed he got down to work. First, he wrapped a table cloth around the shattered head to stop the blood leaving a trail on the floor, then he dragged the heavy body to the back door and left it there while he went and got the pick-up he had hidden around the back. It wasn't easy heaving the gross, lifeless body into the back. The trip back to the farm was uneventful and he was back home and had hidden the body under the straw in his barn before the sun edged above the horizon. He didn't know what to expect. All day long he sat on his porch watching the road that led back to town and savouring the moment when he would be safe from discovery and able to get to work on the corpse. Once the sun set he decided he was in the clear. Nobody had come near the farm. He kept the radio tuned to the local station. They reported the disappearance of the barmaid and said the police suspected foul play and asked anyone with information to come forward. That was good enough for Edward. They weren't looking for him and there was no reason why they should. As soon as night had fallen, he went to the barn and pulled Mary's body from its resting place under the straw. He laid it out on a bench he had specially prepared in one of the barns – his 'operating room'. Quickly the little farmer got to work. He stripped the body and burned the clothes. He then cut off the breasts and filleted her genitalia. These he dropped in preserving jars of formaldehyde. With an axe he chopped off her hands and feet; the feet followed the clothes into the fire, the hands he put in the big new industrial freezer he had recently acquired. With his sharp knife he carefully slit the skin down the spine and along the back of the arms and legs. It was not the way he usually dissected the pigs that he had killed for years but he didn't want to damage the skin. It took him the rest of the night carefully to remove the skin without cutting through it. Tired but happy with a good job well done, he draped the trophy over a couple of poles and retired to bed. When he awoke in the evening he couldn't wait to get back to the grisly business in hand. Lovingly he got all his specimens out and ran them tenderly through his hands. But he had work to do. He took the skin that he had dried out overnight, laid it out on his operating table, stretched it into shape over supple branches he had collected for the job and spent the rest of the evening gently rubbing in rock salt and scrapping away any surplus fat. It was a job needing maximum concentration and by midnight he was exhausted. He gave the skin a last inspection and, satisfied with his evening's work, put everything back in the freezer. Except the pubic area that he was especially interested in. This he took to bed with him.

The disappearance of the barmaid caused a stir in the village but there seemed to be no clues that might shed a light on where she had gone. The blood on the floor behind the bar suggested that she had been injured but nobody had seen anything suspicious and the police soon lost interest. Edward was so happy in his work that he hadn't even bothered to go into town to see how they had reacted to the disappearance. He spent every spare moment with Mary's remains but they were now beginning to look a little second-hand. Besides, he had realised that he had not used the body to its full potential. He decided that he needed another. He didn't deem it prudent to return to the scene of his previous crime but went in the opposite direction. It was a bit farther but he felt that he was cleverly out-thinking the police.

Over the next two years Edward roamed far and wide collecting more specimens. The more he worked on the bodies, the more expert he became in the art of skinning and preserving. He even began to fashion artefacts from parts of the body. He turned skull caps into bowls, stretched skin over a barrel to make a drum. Human lips made original but gruesome bracelets and the genitalia an interesting collar. And the parts of the body that seemed too good to throw away, he cooked and ate. His collection grew at a steady rate. Soon the refrigerator was stuffed with jars of organs, eyes, noses, ears, kidneys. What had been known as 'private parts' were now floating in jars of clear alcohol. But still Edward hadn't got enough. With the acquisitive soul of

a collector, he constantly wanted more. In November 1957, he became friendly with a Bernice Worden who owned a store in Plainsfield, Wisconsin. She was a happy soul and felt sorry for the melancholy little man who seemed to have no friends and nothing to occupy his time. Edward called in at the store to get some antifreeze but Bernice was out of stock. She told him that it was expected in at any moment and he promised to come back and get it. Her son Frank was the deputy sheriff of the town but Edward had been on the murder trail for so long without being caught that this small detail didn't bother him. It gave him an extra thrill to go to the store and chat to the woman and imagine the delights of her body when he had complete control of it back in his special barn on the farm. Son Frank, brought up by his loving mother, also had a weakness for the underdog and treated Edward in a friendly manner. Edward heard him mention to his mother that after he finished his rounds on Saturday he was going fishing with some of the boys and wouldn't be home until supper time. That scrap of information sealed the fate of Bernice Worden. Edward made his usual arrangements to receive a new body, washed down the bench, got rid of any surplus bits and pieces of his previous victims to provide extra storage space and set off to Plainsfield with his pick-up truck. Experience taught him that the best time to strike was at closing time. Then he could go about his work without fear of being interrupted by a customer. Mrs Worden was just hanging up the closed sign when he appeared in the doorway. She smiled, assumed that he had come for the antifreeze he had ordered and let him in. He made a few purchases and then asked if he could look at one of the guns on display. He told her that he was having a lot of trouble with pests on his farm and wanted to buy a rifle. Bernice unlocked the gun rack and handed him the gun. He looked it over and then pointed out another gun he would like to look at. While the woman's back was turned he deftly slipped a bullet he had brought with him into the breach and shot her at point blank range in the back of the head.

Social misfit, farmer Ed Gein, under arrest. (Katz Pictures Ltd)

Quickly, he wrapped her head in some sacks to stop the blood leaving a crimson trail. It was getting dark but he had to wait half an hour before it was dark enough for his purposes. The store was not some isolated shop on the outskirts of the village but slap-bang on the main street. Satisfied that there was nobody likely to see him, he scampered off to recover his pick-up. It was more sophisticated than the wheel barrow he had used for the corpses in the early days and allowed him to range over a far wider area with less chance of being surprised on the road. The back was full of small supply sacks but underneath was just straw. He returned to the back door of the store. It was a matter of minutes to drag out the body and hide it under the sacks. He remembered to pick up his purchases but left the gun on the counter. As he was leaving he noticed the big, ornate cash register. It fascinated him. He opened it, took out the money and put it beside the rifle on the counter. Staggering under the weight, he took the register and placed it in the pick-up beside his victim's body. Ten minutes later he was clear of the village and on the road home.

Frank Worden, the deputy sheriff, returned from his fishing trip to find the store locked up and the door bolted. He called out but got no reply so he went around the back and let himself in. He couldn't find his mother in their living quarters so he went to look in the store. The first thing that he noticed was the cash register was missing. The money on the counter beside the spot where the register had been puzzled him as did the rifle lying beside it. He picked it up and sniffed the barrel. This really worried him. It had been fired recently. He investigated more closely and discovered the small pool of blood behind the counter and the trail leading to the back door. The sacks that Edward had wrapped around Mrs Worden's body had been ineffective in stopping the blood. Frank was shattered and in a highly agitated state called the Sheriff. It didn't take too long to organise a search in the surrounding area. Nobody had seen anything or heard the fatal shot. It was the middle of the

night before the Sheriff called off the search. There wasn't much they could do until the morning when they could have more light and make a thorough search of the surroundings for clues. Frank was still emotionally disturbed by the evidence that his mother had been the victim of foul play and now had to accept that the chances of ever seeing her alive again were pretty minimal. The doctor prescribed a sleeping tonic for him and they all dispersed to their beds to await the morning light. It wasn't until late in the afternoon that the Sheriff showed Frank the bill they had found on the counter. He instantly remembered Edward Gein ordering the antifreeze. It was the first clue they had found and it was to lead them straight to the murderer. Frank wanted to go out to Gein's farm straightaway and confront him. The Sheriff persuaded him to stay in town in case the farmer returned. Reluctantly, Frank agreed.

Edward was in no hurry. Mrs Worden was, of all his victims, the woman he had known best. She was going to be the pinnacle of his art. He had found that when working on a body, it was best to gut it before the natural process of putrefaction set in. He decided to do that before stowing the body in the freezer. Tomorrow he would have a high old time practising the skills he had taught himself over the past few years. To celebrate his latest arrival he sliced her liver and fried it with some potatoes and a garnish of onions. He had just sat down to his meal when he was disturbed by the sound of the Sheriff's car drawing up outside. He put his plate on the side of the stove to keep warm and went outside to greet the Sheriff. The Sheriff told Gein that he was investigating the murder of Bernice Worden and had reason to believe that Gein had been in the store the previous evening shortly before she disappeared. Gein was unflustered by the news and admitted that he had been in the store but claimed that when he left Mrs Worden she had been in perfect health. The Sheriff informed him that he intended to search the farm. Again Gein seemed unaffected even though he must have known that even the most casual search would turn up the trophies that bore witness to his amateur attempts to turn the bodies of 20 or so women into household utensils or articles of apparel. When the Sheriff opened the freezer door it was like looking through the portals of Hell. The disembowelled body of Mrs Worden was hanging upside down from a hook, the gaping wound where Gein had ripped out her intestines, leaking congealed blood. On shelves, bottles with their grisly contents seemed to hover obscenely over him. He had seen enough. Shakily, he closed the door and put a radio call through to his office to get a doctor out to the farm. He knew that it was too late to help any of the victims but he hadn't the stomach for searching through the freezer. Gein didn't seem to be aware of the trouble he was in but tried to chat to the Sheriff whose mind was not on what he was saying. During a search of the house he found chairs covered in what he guessed was human skin. In one of the bedrooms he found a complete female skin with thongs on it so that Gein could wear it about the house. Shin bones had been made into a table lamp with a skin shade. He also found the cash register taken from the store. Gein carefully explained that he hadn't stolen it, he was no thief, he just wanted to investigate how it worked. He seemed to think that this justified his actions.

Once Gein realised that his ghastly crimes were public knowledge, he became anxious that everything should be revealed in every gory facet. The Detectives investigating the case were sickened by the way he was eager to tell them each grisly aspect. There was no problem clarifying even the smallest detail. He had a clear memory of each victim and exactly what he had done with the body. He did make a half-hearted attempt to excuse his behaviour by claiming that the work he was employed on was by way of scientific study. The only thing he didn't claim was that he had been forced to do what he did by voices.

In court he was a model defendant. Once he had got used to being the centre of attention he answered all questions clearly and extensively. His defending counsel at times tried to defuse the bomb craters his client was blowing in any vestige of defence that he might try to put forward in an attempt to mitigate the horrendous nature of his crime. Gein wouldn't have any chamfering of his statements and even argued with his lawyer when he felt forced to make an explanation of his client's circumstances.

Inevitably, Edward Gein was found guilty and sentenced to life in prison. And life meant life. In spite of several attempts at parole, he died of a pulmonary disease in 1984. The farm house that had housed Gein's macabre museum of death became a bit of a tourist attraction for a while but the local inhabitants saw it as a reminder of the terrible crimes that had been committed in their midst and it was shunned. Then one night it caught fire. No attempt was made to save it and it still remains a heap of charred, soot blackened bricks and timber.

Film-makers have always been quick to take advantage of the latest real-life horror story. Ed Gein, the little farmer from the American Midwest township of Plainsfield provided a direct hook-up with at least four films: *Psycho*, *The Texas Chainsaw Massacre*, *Deranged* and *The Silence of the Lambs*. In addition, a film has also been produced called simply *Ed Gein*.

The most cinematically important film to take from the Ed Gein saga was *Psycho*. Made in 1960, it was in direct competition with the onset of Hammer's foray into the world of films horrific. The difference was that Hammer made films for entertainment whereas Hitchcock seemed to be making horror for real. I still remember going and seeing *Psycho* and then going to bed and listening to every creak and sigh, convinced that Norman was coming to get me. *Psycho* took only the incident of Gein's refusal to let his mother be pronounced dead until he was ready to make the break. In the end, Gein did allow his mother's body to be taken away and buried. It was the catalyst that started him on his bloody career. Norman Bates, in *Psycho*, refused to believe his mother was dead and even took over her role when he had something dark and deadly lurking at the back of his mind. Usually brought on by the presence of someone young and nubile. The most well-remembered scene in the film is when dishy but venal Marion Crane (Janet Leigh), trying to escape with the payroll of the company she works for in her handbag, is attacked in the shower and stabbed to death. This scene, and the entire film, is filmed in black and white but this scene is so vividly portrayed that most people who saw it 40 years ago will swear that it was in colour. *Psycho*, by its sophistication and non-reliance on stock horror scene motivations, primed the juices of directors with a macabre bent so that when *The Exorcist* arrived a decade later, it confirmed what had become increasingly evident and took horror and fantasy in another and more financially driven direction.

This probably explains the exploitative title of *The Texas Chainsaw Massacre*. This was another dip into the farmhouse in Plainsfield. In spite of the title, it is a well-conceived script, holding back on the visual horror until it has ran the whole gamut of the traditional fantasy film – the reaction shot. It always works and it is a pity that some directors seem to believe that the most frightening or gut-churning effects can be achieved by letting it all gush out. This in itself is curious because *The Texas Chainsaw Massacre* came right at the beginning of the slash and gush era and it should have pointed the way ahead. The story starts with news that grandpappy's grave has been the target of vandals. Peppy Sally, played

straight by Marilyn Burns, decides to return to the family home base to see what's going on. She takes her wheelchair-bound brother, Franklin (Paul Partain) with her. When they get to the old homestead they find it is being vandalised by a nearby family which still harbours a grudge against grandpappy and his descendants. The family is into murder, maiming, incest and all the things for which earthly, caring farmer families in the American Midwest are not traditionally known. Leader of the family is Leatherface, (Gunnar Hansen) who hides behind a grotesque mask made from human flesh and is given to wielding a mean chainsaw. The inside of the farmhouse is decorated by the same decorator who was the inspiration for real-life Ed Gein's approach to *House and Garden*. It's hard to understand why anyone would want to adorn their house with the leftover parts of a defunct body, human or beastly, but it is surprising how many quite normal-looking people do.

Another film in the Ed Gein vein is *Deranged*. Made in 1974, this tries to tell the story of Gein but decides that the facts are not enough. It has the Ed character, Ezra Cobb, mummifying his mum and then going on a murder spree to find suitable companions for her. The most memorable scene in this film is the macabre dinner party with the mummified and rotting diners sitting around the table. It is a well-constructed oeuvre that somehow gives the terrible events and Cobb's bizarre sense of right and wrong a twisted logic. It also gives make-up artist Tom Savini a great chance to run wild with the latex rubber and Max Factor.

6
Dr Geza de Kaplany

Not all certifiable killers go off on a multiple spree. Some just funnel all their foulness into a few short hours. Dr de Kaplany stepped out of the role of medical healer and into the murderer category in one insane hour. The doctor had many friends from all walks of life. Although he was arrogant and egotistical, he knew the value of having access to people who could further his career. He was an anaesthesiologist. He had emigrated with his parents from Hungary when he was a teenager. His parents doted on him and worked all hours to scrape together enough money to send their son through college and then support him at medical school. He kept on good terms with the San Josè Hungarian population and was happy to help out whenever there was a problem. His 'scalpel for hire' philosophy made him rich and he began to move in more influential circles. His willingness to use his more unorthodox medical skills for the benefit of his friends became widely known among the glitteratti and when he wasn't working at the hospital was always on call for anything that he would be unable to countenance in his day job. This brought him into contact with erring politicians and actors and actresses who couldn't or didn't want their secrets exposed to the critical gaze of the general public. At the height of his fame he fell in love with a beautiful Hungarian model, Hajna. He was crazy about her and wouldn't leave her alone until she consented to marry him. It was probably the promises he made of the advantages to be gained by becoming the wife of a doctor who knew the secrets of the rich and powerful. Once the knot was tied, de Kaplany showed his true colours. He forbade Hajna from working as a model. At first Hajna didn't mind too much. The excitement of the photo-shoot and the catwalk were replaced by glittering parties and easy access to the Hollywood set. Unfortunately, she enjoyed the parties too well and had to endure the bad-tempered criticisms of her behaviour on the way home. These became so scurrilous that Hajna refused to go out with him. Her high-flying husband couldn't have that. He enjoyed the envy of his friends when he appeared with the beautiful Hungarian on his arm. Besides, then he wouldn't be in control. Who knows what she would get up to while he was away in the evening. He fanticised a Catherine of Russia situation with a queue of young horny Hussars filing into his bedroom and riding his beautiful wife. Now the nightly outings were ill-tempered affairs. Hajna made no attempt to disguise the distaste she had for her husband's company and deliberately flirted with anyone who took her fancy. de Kaplany smouldered but there was little he could to do about the situation. The pressure of work and his wife's indifference brought on impotency. A terrible humiliation for the gallant doctor who saw himself a swordsman to rival the Kennedys. This caused him to be even more suspicious of his nubile young wife who taunted him about his sexual inadequacy.

He needed help but he was too bloody minded to go and tell one of his more specialised colleagues his problem and get expert help. The burden of his secret work away from the hospital, his nightly jags with the likes of the Kennedys and their film friends, the nagging fear that he was being cuckolded and his feeling of inferiority brought on by his impotency took him to the edge of a mental breakdown. What drove him over the edge was his knowledge of a crime which he was instrumental in bringing about. He convinced himself that his knowledge was power. Nobody could touch him. Now all he had to do was fix his wife so that he no longer had to question her fidelity and he could live happily and comfortably ever after.

He laid his plans carefully. First, he purchased a high-powered stereo with ancillary speakers. He distributed these around the apartment saying that he wanted to be able to hear music wherever he went. His relationship with his wife was so bad now that she took no notice and didn't question the fact that there were so many speakers. From the hospital he started to remove small bottles of acid. These he stored in his refrigerator in a locked metal box. Although he had planned what he was going to do to bring his glamorous wife to heel, it was on an 'if' basis. If she wouldn't see sense and give up her suspected life of debauchery, he was going to fix it so that no one ever fancied her again. Hajna sealed her fate by spending a few minutes on the balcony talking to a young actor. They were happy and at ease with each other and de Kaplany was convinced they were having an affair, although he had no evidence to substantiate his fear.

All night he lay awake thinking about what he proposed to do to stop his beautiful wife running off with somebody else to find sexual satisfaction. Not for a moment did he consider that what he was doing would be the end of him as a doctor and as a free man. He was sure that with what he knew about his high-powered friends he would be invulnerable. He watched his wife rise and take a shower and smiled to himself as she drank a freshly squeezed orange juice and nibbled at a thin slice of toast. He saw the funny side of her dieting to keep her fantastic figure when it would shortly be no more. He waited until she returned to the bedroom. Now it became obvious why he had bought the powerful record player. He locked the doors and turned up the sound so that the air seemed to shake with the pounding music. Quickly he stripped off, put on an all enveloping rubber apron and gloves and went into the bedroom. Hajna eyed him coldly, unable to share the joke of the overpowering music and his fancy dress. He made no villainous threats. Just threw her on to the bed. She fought him as he tried to tie her hands but a well-aimed blow to the head daze her and before she could recover she was spread-eagled on the bed, naked. Her wrists and ankles securely taped to the bedposts.

de Kaplany went quickly to work. He knew that it wasn't going to be long before his neighbours came to complain about the music. He took the bottles of acid from the refrigerator and lined them up on the bedside table. Next, he placed a tray on a chair next to the bed and lined up a variety of scalpels. All under the horrified gaze of his bound wife who was beginning to realise that this was more than just a sexual game her husband was playing in an effort to kick-start his flagging libido. She pleaded with him to untie her, promised to talk and try to come to some mutually respected arrangement. de Kaplany just smiled and gestured towards the loudspeakers, miming that he couldn't hear because of the loudness of the music. He made the first incision with his shiny scalpel across her stomach, splitting the belly button and severing the lean muscles that gave her such a wonderful shape. Fussily, he picked up one of the bottles of acid and poured the contents into the wounds. The cries of the tortured woman when the incision was made were nothing compared with her screams when the acid burned into her flesh. de Kaplany nodded satisfaction. It was a start. The next neat incision was down her nose. When he poured in the acid, his wife's frenzied squirming made it run down her face and into her eyes. It would have been a blessing if the pain had pushed her into unconsciousness but instead it kept her awake. The doctor had now got a taste for his deadly surgery. He sliced open her breasts and poured in more acid, savagely ripped open her vagina and emptied more acid into the womb. Still the once-beautiful woman refused to die or lapse into unconsciousness. By now her agonised screams were reaching a higher degree of decibels than the multiple speakers situated around the apartment. Neighbours who were already agitated by the disturbance of their usually placid life by the music now became aware of the ear-piercing screams. They met outside the doctor's door and in approved indignant neighbour style pounded on the panel and demanded ingress. The doctor was beyond entertaining neighbours. Cutting and pouring, he had reduced most of his wife's once glorious body to a mass of hideous raw tissue and mutilated, still smoking flesh. The neighbours had a quick powwow and decided it was time to call in the police. Ten minutes later police officers were threatening to break the door down unless de Kaplany opened it at once. Just as they were about to carry out their threat the music ceased abruptly. Again, they called for the doctor to open the door. Slowly the door opened and de Kaplany stood before them still wearing his rubber apron and gloves. He smiled apologetically and explained that he was a doctor and had been engaged on an experiment and had not heard them hammering on the door because of the music. He might have got away with no more than a caution about the noise if his victim hadn't screamed at that moment. The doctor shrugged as if it was all part of his on-going experiment and tried to close the door. The police officers decided that they needed to have a look. They could apologise later. What they found in the bedroom was to haunt their nights for years to come. The once-beautiful woman was still tied to the bedposts. Her face was something out of a nightmare. Where the doctor had slit the flesh and poured the highly corrosive acid into the wounds, the skin had peeled away leaving bubbling, obscene white strands that seeped blood. Her cheeks had disappeared leaving only the grey decalcifying bone. White smoke from the acid seemed to float above the surface of the ravaged skin but did nothing to hide the hideous wounds. Where the acid had run down her face and into her eye sockets it had melted the eyes leaving only a residue of collapsed tissue. The rest of her body seemed

to writhe and squirm as the acid, still active, cut inexorably into the living flesh. Hajna was still conscious but delirious with pain. de Kaplany made no attempt to escape. His feeble attempt to explain to the police officers that he did not intend to kill his wife, merely disfigure her so that she would be unattractive to other men, went unnoticed by the nauseous men. The officers were at a loss as to know how to deal with the situation. They untied Hajna and tried to make her comfortable, ignoring the pain when the acid came into contact with their bare hands. They were relieved when the medical team arrived and they could place the tormented woman in expert hands and turn their attention to her husband.

He was still trying to convince them that the dreadful torture he had visited on his wife was her own fault. That he had been forced to chastise her for her own sake. What loving husband wouldn't if he was interested in keeping his marriage alive? It was three agonising weeks before the Hungarian beauty gave up the fight. In spite of all the efforts of the hospital staff, secondary infection set in and she died a suppurating mass of scar tissue. The newspapers had a field day. The bizarre and tragic event made the front page of practically every paper in the United States and many beyond. The trial was awaited with ghoulish anticipation. Details of the crime had, of necessity, been sparse but enough had leaked out to forecast a truly unusual time in court. de Kaplany acted as if he couldn't understand what the problem was. To anyone who would listen he explained that he had no intention of taking the life of his wife and only wanted to teach her a lesson. As the day for the trial drew closer, he changed his attitude. He no longer tried to convince anyone of his innocence. He began to boast that he had friends in high places. That these 'friends' had a vested interest in not seeing him punished. He hinted that these same 'friends' were in a position to see that any sentence he received would he set aside very quickly. In the courtroom he had another change of heart. Now he played the distraught husband who,

Dr Geza de Kaplany uses his scalpel and acid to make his wife Jajna unattractive to other men.

through overwork and a medical condition which manifested itself in his documented impotency, had a momentary lapse into insanity. A moment that had lasted an hour and resulted in the tragic death of his beloved wife. He might have had a chance. Whoever could have performed the terrible act of desecration on another human being would seem to have a prima facie case for claiming to be mad. Except that he had prepared for the day in meticulous detail. The photographs of his wife's body finished any chance he might of had of being packed off to a nice little sanatorium and forgotten. After looking at them the jurors had to retire to regain control of their emotions. The doctor appeared to be in complete control of himself. He reiterated his claim that he had no intention of killing his wife – just make her unattractive to other men. It didn't take the jury long to reach a verdict. Guilty as charged. He was handed down a life sentence.

Now a number of strange events started to kick in. de Kaplany was classified a 'special category prisoner'. This is a euphemism usually reserved for people convicted of a felony but, because they have some special knowledge or are for some reason a security risk, are given special treatment. It could be argued that after the terrible crime he had committed, it was thought wise by the authorities that he should be kept segregated for his own safety. This does not appear to be the case. A scandal was in the making when, six months before the time set for his first parole hearing, he was suddenly released. Whether the authorities expected him to be forgotten or not isn't clear. If they did, they were mistaken. It was too good a story to let alone and the reporters began writing stories about the Acid Doctor, a monster who had committed crimes that defied logic and decency, and was being let loose on the vulnerable public without serving his time. Attacked on all sides the administration tried to claim that de Kaplany, a 'cardiac specialist' was being released early as his expertise was needed in Taiwan. This was such a flagrant

misrepresentation of the facts that the newspapers found it difficult to adjust their attitude. de Kaplany had suddenly become a heart specialist without any trace of having worked in this sphere. And there was such a shortage of specialists in Taiwan that a homicidal doctor from California was let out of jail to try to satisfy the need? The head of the review board that had been set up to review the case couldn't take it. Whatever the background machinations were to spring de Kaplany, and the reasons were probably known to him, he was obviously disgusted at the distortion of justice that he was being asked to accept. Whatever the reason was for de Kaplany's unexpected release, it was too late to do anything about it. Before the first headline had been written, Kaplany was smuggled out of the country and had taken up residence in Taiwan.

There are a few interesting features to the case – other than the horrific facts. Marilyn Monroe was found dead in nearby San Josè. Her death was described as suicide and the evidence was the empty bottle that had contained Nembutal tablets, found in her hand. The date – 4 August 1962 – just three weeks before Dr de Kaplany decided to chastise his wife. Three months later, President Kennedy was shot and de Kaplany began a life sentence which he was sure would be curtailed as soon as his high-flying friends got on the job. Then in 1975, a decidedly dodgy time in American politics, the messy aftermath of the Watergate Scandal and Nixon's impeachment and the revelation that Robert Kennedy was behind several attempts to assassinate Cuban President Castro, plus the mire of the Vietnam War and the continuing suggestion that the Kennedy Administration hadn't been the pure base for an Arthurian revival that many had claimed, Dr de Kaplany was released. What's more – in spite of his record, he was assisted in finding work in the medical field, although apparently grossly under-qualified, by the new administration. What does all this mean? Don't know! But it is interesting.

7
Marcel Andre Henri Felix Petiot

As if Europe, and France in particular, didn't have enough to cope with in the early 1940s, they also had Petiot. How he ever got to be a doctor is an on-going mystery. His first ambition was to be a soldier and as soon as he was old enough, he went to the recruiting office in Auxerre and offered his services. It was the height of the First World War, the war to end war – and the Recruiting Sergeant was happy to sign up the eager recruit. Marcel was posted to Normandy for training and proved to be an excellent soldier. When it was time for him to be posted to the front, he claimed that he was a medical student and that he had worked with his father, a physician, since he was 14 and had a lot of experience in caring for patients. The army authorities were not too picky. The daily total of men blown apart by shells or shot by sniper fire was so high that it hardly seemed worth going to all the bother of checking credentials. Petiot was made a medical orderly and pushed up towards the front line to serve in the battalion field hospital. He was an eager, hard-working member of the hospital staff and there were no complaints about his work. Before long, his industry brought rewards. The hard-pressed doctors were happy to let him take some of the work off their hands and he was performing minor operations and prescribing drugs. Once established, Petiot saw the chances of making a bit of money on the side. With open access to the drugs cabinet, he was soon making a lot of money selling what are now known as recreational drugs to the battle-traumatised troops and local inhabitants only too eager to have a

few moments drug-granted bliss away from the peril of being non-combatants in a combative situation. Now that he was in business for himself, his work began to get sloppy and he was often absent when he was needed. It was during one of his absences that his creative accountancy with the drug records was noticed. The officer in charge of the medical supplies realised that the treatment of Petiot, particularly with regard to granting him unlimited control over the drug supplies, would not look good on his record if the facts came out in a Court Martial. So for the sake of all concerned he claimed that Petiot was suffering from psychoneurosis and kicked him out. Petiot had enjoyed his experience working in the field hospital and decided he would like to become a real doctor. His father worked for the post office and had risen to the position of Supervisor of Post. He had been worried about his son for some time and was happy to help out when he came to him and told him he wanted to become a doctor. He made arrangements to pay him a small allowance and packed him off to medical university in Paris. The experienced ex-soldier with as much practical experience as some of the resident doctors was a good communicator. Before long he had a large group of acquaintants. In 1921 he received his degree and left Paris to take up a practice in Villeneuve. His mental state was a little fragile but he was aware of it and able to keep his feelings under control. He became a part of the community and a trusted member of the town council. When the position of Mayor became vacant, it seemed natural that the good doctor should be put

Petiot claimed that all the murders were in the interest of France. (Hulton Deutsch)

forward. He showed a becoming reluctance to take on the honour but as there was no serious opposition to his candidacy, he soon found himself the leader of the community.

The high-profile job was not in Petiot's interest. In spite of his new found position of head carer and leader of the people, he was still the man who had stolen vital drugs from the meagre hospital supplies and sold them on the black market. His new position gave him unimpeded access to an unlimited supply of a wide variety of drugs and a circle of acquaintances eager to buy them from him. The first irritant to spoil his plans came from his housekeeper. She was pregnant and claimed that Petiot was the father. Not only that, but said that he had come to her bedroom in the night and raped her. She had kept quiet, she claimed, because he had promised to marry her. Petiot dismissed the claim. He said that he had been aware that the woman had been seeing some unknown man for some time. When she found she was pregnant, she came to him and asked him to perform an abortion. Although sympathetic to her dilemma, he had refused. She had taken his sympathy for weakness and had threatened to tell everyone that he was the father if he wouldn't do what was necessary. He had again refused and she had started spreading the rumour that he was the father of the unborn child. It wasn't a big thing in French public life and many would have been surprised if he hadn't been having an occasional bit of hanky panky with his live-in housekeeper. But more revelations were to follow. One of his patients accused him of stealing from her home while she was bedridden. He strongly denied the accusation and claimed that he had seen one of the servants with the necklace he was supposed to have stolen. But he had trodden on a number of influential toes in his position of Maire and others, hearing what he had been suspected of, came forward with claims of their

own. The hospital called him in to explain why the accounts for the purchase of drugs and medical equipment did not balance. He blamed this on the inefficiency of his staff and promised to look into the matter. The hospital board patiently waited for the revised figures to arrive but then lost patience with his prevarications and ordered an inquiry. He was found guilty and sent to prison for six months. Madame Debauvre had been a patient of Petiot since he first arrived in the town and had been an ardent supporter even when he was accused of theft and sent to prison. She had made a will naming the doctor as one of the beneficiaries. Out of jail the doctor was in financial trouble. When Madame Debauvre developed a chest infection, Petiot was constantly at her side. In spite of, or because of, his attention, the lady died. Petiot was now a disgraced figure in the community. A witness came forward, Madame Debauvre's cook, Therese Lecasec, who alleged that she had seen the doctor, in the kitchen of the Debauvre house, take out a green bottle containing a powered substance and mix it into the food she had prepared for her mistress. She had not thought anything of it at the time as she was aware that some poisons were used in a good many household items. Fortunately, before the case could come to trial, Therese died. With no other witness to point a finger and no forensic evidence to suggest that his patient's death was from other than natural causes, the prosecution was abandoned.

Petiot decided it was time to move on. He went back to his old haunts in Paris and earned a living doing abortions and looking after patients who would prefer not to get caught up in the legal side of the medical profession. He surfaced again a few years later when he was arrested for robbing a book shop. He protested loudly and claimed it was all an oversight. Why would he, a respected doctor, stoop to stealing books? The police made enquiries and discovered that he was indeed a doctor and released him. He now rented a house in Paris and got down to some legitimate doctoring. Then the Nazis marched into Paris and Petiot knew that it was time to strike out and build up his client base. He bought a large detached house on the other side of town and began making alterations. There was no doubt that when he designed the new interior for his house he had murder on his mind. At the centre of the building, well insulated from the rest of the house, was his murder room. He had specially built culverts replacing the old-fashioned drains. These ran straight into the main sewers. Behind the house was a compost burner but it was like no other compost burner in an ordinary garden. To keep his activities out of sight of prying eyes he surrounded the house with a high wall topped with barbed wire. Into the side wall he had an iron-studded door built wide enough for lorries to pass through. This door was to see a lot of use over the next year or so. Neighbours later reported that often at night a lorry would arrive and be let in through the gates instantly. The lorries had no markings but were assumed to be German military vehicles by the neighbours. But these same neighbours had enough on their plates without worrying about what the doctor was doing. They weren't as lucky as he was to have friends in the army of occupation. Then in 1944, the police received a complaint about the smell that even Petiot's enclosure wall couldn't contain. A policeman was dispatched to have a word with the doctor and suggest he might clean his drains or whatever it was that was creating the nuisance. Petiot refused to let the officer in but promised to have his drains examined. The weather got warmer and the smell stronger. This time when the police arrived Petiot didn't even answer the door. The Inspector ordered the Fire Brigade out and they forced open the door. The police went into the house. It was dark and silent – and the stench unbelievable. It didn't take them long to find the source. In the special room at the centre of the house were piled dozens of corpses in varying stages of decomposition. Further searches revealed more bodies as well as piles of clothing and a huge amount of money and jewellery, and Dr Petiot. Petiot had made plans for just such a moment. He took the Inspector aside and explained that he was a member of the Resistance. He appealed to the patriotism of the Inspector to listen to him before doing anything hasty. With the Allies already en route for Paris, the Inspector was happy to listen. If Petiot was who he said he was, it wouldn't do the Inspector any harm to have a friend in the Resistance when the liberators arrived. Quickly, Petiot explained that the bodies were those of Nazi collaborators. He had been ordered to get rid of them before they could become a nuisance when the invading armies freed the capital. The policeman thought about it and decided to give him the benefit of doubt. Petiot suggested that he returned the following day with another officer who he could be sure of and Petiot would introduce them to a member of the Resistance who would be able to vouch for him. The Inspector agreed. As soon as the policemen left, Petiot gathered up as much as he could of his loot and went across town to his home and picked up his wife and teenage son. When the Inspector returned the following day, all he discovered was a stench and the heaps of decaying bodies. Petiot was conspicuous by his absence. Petiot and his family went to stay in a farmhouse owned by his wife's family in Evreux. France was in such a state that nobody questioned a refugee family moving into the district. Especially as they had somewhere to live and weren't going to be a burden.

Rumours of the atrocities that had taken place in the house on rue Lesueur circulated. At first, the stories told of the gallant members of the Resistance who had taken out members of the German High Command to facilitate the Allies' advance. Later, the

Petiot dispatches another refugee who put his trust in him.

rumours changed. It was said that Petiot was a German sympathiser, that the house had been bought with Nazi gold and used as an extermination centre, by the Nazis, to get rid of any Resistance workers caught in the Paris area. This rumour became the ranking rumour and eventually got to the ears of Petiot in his country bolt hole. Indignant and wanting to clear his position before the liberators began a witch hunt, Petiot wrote to a Paris newspaper and claimed that the vicious stories about his collaboration with the Nazis were a frame up by the Nazis. When General de Gaulle walked down the Champs Elysses and declared Paris free, Petiot decided it was time to return to Paris. It wouldn't be long before the upright French citizens would be out hunting for German sympathisers and it would be easier to isolate him in the little hamlet of Evreux than in the post-occupation turmoil of Paris. He altered his appearance and tried to mingle unnoticed in the bustling masses. But the eyes of the righteous were bright and in November, a little over two months after the Nazis quit Paris, he was spotted on the street and followed back to the rooms he had taken in rue Faubourge St Denis. He was lucky to survive the streets and be taken to police headquarters. At this time the good citizens of Paris were still settling scores with anyone denounced as being a friend of the departed German Army.

Doctor Petiot still put forward his claim that he had worked with the Resistance throughout the occupation and proved that he had been a part of the Free French Forces operating in Paris under the name of Captain Henri Valery – this was checked and validated. But his membership of the undercover group had lasted for only six weeks and it was after this time that the bodies found in his house in rue Lesueur were murdered. Petiot claimed that he had tortured and killed over 60 Nazi sympathisers and members of the occupying force on the direct orders of the Resistance leaders. Often these orders were

relayed to him through the BBC Overseas Broadcasts. He was asked to supply the names of his colleagues in the Resistance but he refused saying that there were still too many traitors in the country who would benefit from their exposure.

The French Police, after a preliminary investigation, discarded the premise that he shouldn't be touched because he was a member of the Resistance. They also discarded the idea that he was in the pay of the Nazis to do away with members of the Resistance. They indicted him on the good old-fashioned charges of theft, torture and murder. They proved that Petiot had amassed a fortune by offering to spirit French Jews out of France to safety in Britain. To pay for this privilege he charged only a modest fee to cover his overheads. He collected the Jews from various parts of the city, where they were hiding, in a lorry that had been loaned him by the Germans to pick up supplies for the hospital where he worked on a rota basis during the weekend. Once in the house, the Jews were led one by one to the murder room and their possessions stripped from them. They were then asked where they had hidden the rest of their wealth. If they protested that they didn't have anything else, they were tortured until they revealed all or Petiot believed that he had really got everything they owned. The outcome was always the same. The unfortunate refugee was then either strangled or bludgeoned to death.

As successful as Petiot was at getting the refugees to his house, he ran into the same problem as the Nazis did in the concentration camps. The efficient disposal of the bodies. When Petiot built the small furnace he assumed that it would be a relatively easy task to burn the bodies to ashes and sluice the ashes away down his specially constructed drain. He soon learned that it isn't that easy to dispose of a body. The more successful he was at acquiring bodies, the greater his chances of being discovered became. At last the stench called attention to what was happening and Petiot was caught – red-handed. More damning evidence came from a small building he still owned in Villeneuve. Nearly 50 suitcases and other items were discovered there and linked back to their owners.

Dr Petiot was sentenced to death. It was estimated that he had accrued a fortune of over £1,000,000 during the four years of the Nazis occupation by his operation of the house in rue Lesueur. There was some suspicion that what had been common knowledge at the end of the war might have had a grain of truth. The suspicion that Petiot had some connection with the Nazis was not pursued but it was generally acknowledged that it seemed highly unlikely that he could have rebuilt the house as a virtual fortress, run a German Army truck and moved so freely about the city without the co-operation of at least someone in authority among the Occupying Forces.

Dr Petiot was sentenced to death in April 1946 and guillotined a month later without confessing to his crimes.

8

Dr Mengele

In the entire history of cold-blooded murderers there has never been anyone to compete with Dr Mengele for the supreme title. There have been people who tortured and maimed for pleasure. Those who decided that money was worth the torture and death of a fellow human being. Jealousy has caused men and women to commit the most horrendous crimes and even love has been known to be a motive for murder. The Spanish Inquisition was notorious for its torture and execution of innocent people who dared to differ in their religious ideology. Military machismo has goaded normal men into performing murderous tasks that cannot be excused by the fact that the victims were the enemy. Just being in the wrong place at the wrong time is often enough of an excuse for an unbalanced character to commit murder. Then there is murder by mistake and murder for pleasure. None of these instances can be condoned but in some cases a mitigating circumstance can be found, if not accepted. In the case of Mengele, nothing can be said in his defence that could ameliorate the hideous crimes he committed in the name of medical science.

Josef Mengele was born in Gunsberg in Germany in 1911. In Munich, where he was studying philosophy, he came under the influence of Alfred Rosenberg. In spite of his name, Rosenberg was a radical supporter of the doctrine of Aryan superiority. He was one of the guiding lights of National Socialism and an early member of the Nazi Party. Mengele lapped up everything Rosenberg told him and determined that he would make it his life's work to enhance the standing of the Aryan Race. At Frankfurt University, where he studied medicine, he was known as an eager student, intelligent but not a good

mixer. As soon as he was qualified, he offered his services to the Nazi party.

When Mengele arrived in the Auschwitz Concentration Camp in May 1943, it was already a place of 'experiments'. These experiments were conducted on prisoners and were the sort of tests that were used by the Wehrmacht and other bodies interested in finding the parameters of human endurance. The British Army used soldiers to test out drugs. These were usually with the compliance of the guinea pigs but sometimes they were coerced into volunteering to get off a worse fate for which some real or trumped up misdemeanour had put them in line. Exposure to the elements to record how the body reacted and what was the best method to combat the after effects was very popular. Research on the common cold was also popular and civilians as well as military personal volunteered to be part of the programme for a small fee. Later, there were even experiments to see what reaction the body had to being exposed to such things as anthrax and radiation. By and large these experiments were carried out with the best of intentions and the subjects were well treated and were sent on their way with few or no after effects. At Auschwitz similar tests were carried out but with less respect for the health of the subject. But, harsh though the regime was, in many cases it was better to be a specimen than suffer the alternative – candidature for the gas chamber and the furnace. Mengele changed all that. He looked on the prisoners as a chance to conduct experiments that would make his name a by-word for pushing the boundaries of medical research to strata never before envisaged. There was no honeymoon period while he settled in. As soon as his orderly had unpacked his white overall, he went to the small railway yard where daily long trains of Jews, Gypsies, homosexuals and others categorised as unacceptable by the Nazi party, arrived. He soon had the system for selecting those who could be of some use to the Third Reich and those only fit for the gas chamber down to a fine art. As the prisoners shuffled passed him, near death from many hours in a cattle truck without heat, food, water or sanitation, with a flick of the finger he would point the way either to immediate death or a slow death with the slightest chance of salvation. He was particularly interested in twins, especially identical twins. The prospect of experiments in which he could use one of the twins as a control and measure the differences on the other after being subjected to his research, excited him. In all he selected 15,000 twins for his experiments. Only 200 were to survive the end of the war. And all of them bore the marks of their time in the hands of the monster who had sworn to nurture, not murder, his fellow man. One of the experiments he picked up that was already underway was the tolerance of the human form to heat and cold. So far the tests had been conducted with the idea that the subject was released while he was still alive. This wasn't good enough for Mengele. The Führer wanted to know how ditched airman could be guarded against death from hypothermia when their plane was shot down into icy water, how long they would last and what could be done for them once they were picked up. Burns were also a source of tremendous suffering. Mengele had prisoners confined, naked, in tanks of freezing water and timed how long it took them to die. Once they had expired the body was hauled out of the tank and every effort was made to resuscitate the body. A successful resuscitation did not guarantee the subject freedom from further experimentation. Rather the reverse. He had survived where others died. Mengele wanted to know why. Usually, it was enough to qualify the prisoner for an experiment in the hot tank. The same tank was pressed into operation but this time the temperature of the water was gradually raised and the reaction of the subject duly noted. When Mengele calculated that the subject had reached the end of his, or her, tolerance they were taken from the scalding liquid and experiments were conducted to see if they could be saved. Mengele was a staunch supporter of vivisection and many of his patients were cut to pieces while they were still alive to gratify some whim of the doctor that he felt couldn't be satisfied by a post mortem. It did not take Josef Mengele long to earn the sobriquet of 'The Angel of Death'. Although where his angelic side was demonstrated is hard to understand.

Eyes were of special interest. If twins were found with eyes of a different colour or with eyes differing from the eyes of their parents, he was really excited. He tried experiments with dyes injected straight into the iris to see if the colour of the eye could be permanently altered. He also did experiments with eye grafts. He claimed that a graft taken from a live subject and transferred to another had a better chance of not being rejected if the operation was performed without anaesthetic. He also tried transplanting an eye from one twin into the other. The success rate was recorded as nil. He had an on-going interest in transplanting organs of all sorts. Even whole bodies – if that can be called an organ. He had one set of twins slit open, their organs interconnected and then sewn up again. Their mother and father were also in the special experimental wing and when they saw the suffering of their children, they suffocated them to put them out of their agony. When Mengele heard about it he ordered the parents to undergo the same operation – without anaesthetic. Mercifully, they both died before the hideous operation was completed.

The doctor now turned his attention to physical deformity. His boss Heinrich Himmler was always keen to have proof that the Jews were a sub-species and wanted to be kept informed of any experiments that might authenticate his supposition. Mengele was happy

Josef Mengele wanted to be remembered as a doctor who pushed back the frontiers of medical science.

to oblige. A family was brought to the ramp. There were three dwarves and two normal-sized people. Mengele saw this as an exceptional opportunity to study a family that had an abnormality that only became evident in certain members of the group. He took samples from all of their organs and compared them; there seemed to be no difference between them. He then came to the conclusion that the condition was passed on through the mother. He began a series of experiments on the vaginas and wombs of the female dwarves. Still he could come to no conclusion that might account for the abnormalities. Teeth extracted from the whole family were sent to Berlin for analysis. By now Dr Mengele was considered the foremost authority on twins and deformity and he was able to make use of the University facilities whenever he wanted something examined that couldn't be undertaken in the camp. He was unable to determine what exactly was the cause of dwarfism but didn't want to let his protracted experiments go to waste. He invited SS Officers from all over the Reich to come and see his dwarves. They arrived in numbers. Mengele had the dwarves stripped and put on display like exhibits in a freak show. As an interesting side bar, Mengele had taken great pains to construct an illuminated family tree so that his fellow officers could appreciate the finer points of his research. Later the dwarves were forced to perform the circus act they had done before the war – in the nude. The nudity, it was explained, was to show those interested the way the muscles worked in the stunted body. If that was the reason, Mengele had seriously miscalculated the interests of those present. After the performance the women were sexually abused and used as play-things.

When a father and son arrived, the father with severe curvature of the spine and the son with a club foot, Mengele took this as another opportunity to find the rogue gene that was the basis for all deformity. After a long oral examination of the two, Mengele had them shot and their bodies boiled in water to remove the flesh. The bones were then carefully tagged and sent to the Berlin Anthropological Museum for exhibition.

The sight of Josef Mengele riding around the camp on his bicycle was enough to bring fear to the bravest heart. Many who escaped selection on the ramp for the gas chamber were unlucky enough to attract Mengele's attention as they slaved around the camp. One man who had slipped through unnoticed was working digging a trench when Mengele rode up and, quite by chance, stopped opposite him. The man kept his head down and shovelled even faster. Mengele was about to ride off when he noticed the man's hands. He jumped off his bike and scrambled into the trench. When he left, the man went with him back to the laboratories under escort. Mengele had noticed something that the prisoner had managed to keep hidden for a long time – he had six fingers on each hand. That was enough to set the doctor off on a series of experiments that only stopped when the man's heart gave out. Mengele was disappointed but made the best of a bad job, cut off the six-fingered hands and sent them off to the museum in Berlin as an exhibit presented by SS Captain Doctor Josef Mengele. Most of the doctor's undertakings were guided by some sort of macabre logic. Just occasionally he did something that was hard to fathom. The prisoners were on parade waiting for their Kapos to send them off to work. Mengele turned up on his bicycle and stood watching. Just as they were about to move off, Mengele thrust his bicycle at a guard and called to the Kapo to wait. He was obviously in a fuming rage about something but gave no indication what had caused his ill humour. He marched furiously along the ranks of cowering prisoners until he came to a tall, good-looking teenager. He grabbed him by the shoulder and pulled him out of the line. He called one of the guards over and ordered him to bring a board, a hammer and some nails. The youth stood shaking in his shoes while the soldier rushed off to do his superior's bidding. He returned a few minutes later with the items Mengele wanted. Mengele marched the terrified prisoner across to some goal posts used by the soldiers

The Nazi version of the Grim Reaper.

for recreation. He thrust the prisoner against the post and instructed the Kapo to nail the board in place directly above his head. Thankfully, the prisoner was allowed to go back to the ranks. Mengele then ordered all the prisoners to walk under the board sticking out at a right-angle from the goal post. Those not making the grade were ordered to one side and then taken to the gas chamber. Those who were as tall or taller than the marker board were ordered back to work. Mengele got back on his bicycle and cycled off serenely.

Unlike many of his Nazi colleagues, Mengele was not particularly afraid of the advancing Allied troops. He assumed that when his work was explained to the Opposition's medical staff, they would see the merit of his experiments and congratulate him on pushing back the barriers of science. When the order came to start destroying the evidence of his war work, he at first refused to comply. It was only after a direct order from his boss and friend, Himmler, that he began to see that maybe the soft-shelled Allies might not be able to see the benefits he could bestow on the master races by his experiments on the sub-classes. Once he had the idea in his head that he wouldn't be asked to read his papers at the medical centres of the world, he didn't hang about. When the Americans rolled into Auschwitz and saw the enormity of the crime committed there, Mengele was long gone. He had bought himself a passage on one of the Argentinean ships leaving Portugal. All he had to do was blend into the chaos of war-ravaged Europe, join the thousands of refugees trying to find a home, get into Portugal where he could be sure of friends willing to smuggle him aboard ship, and he was home free. He did have a few moments of anxiety. On a couple of occasions he was stopped by troops but was able to talk himself out of trouble. Once he was picked up and interviewed by an English officer but he was able to give such a good account of his life in a prison camp as a guest of the Nazis that they sent him on his way with a bar of chocolate and an army blanket. When he hit the South American sub-continent he disappeared without trace. He was thought to be living in Paraguay or Uruguay or Brazil. He was even reported as being a resident of Buenos Aires in Argentina. Nothing is really known of his whereabouts. The generally accepted theory was that he died in the 1960s under the name of Wolfgang Gerhard. Then a body was found in Paraguay that was claimed as that of the Angel of Death. For a generation, spotting Mengele or his partner in crime, Martin Borman, was an international pastime. It's still possible that Mengele is an old man sweating out his last years in a Paraguayan jungle or stomping on his zimmer frame along the long hot avenues of Buenos Aires. But I doubt it.

9
Drs Teet Haerm and Lars Thomas

It's amazing how often the person you would least expect to be a murderer is guilty of the most outrageous crimes. Doctors, respected internationally, turn up again and again with blood on their hands that doesn't always come from the operating theatre. Significantly, doctors also have one of the highest suicide rates of any profession. Dr Teet Haerm was just such a monster. His friend and colleague, Dr Lars Thomas, appears to have been just a weak character who was overwhelmed by the malignant but persuasive nature of Haerm.

The body of a 30-year-old prostitute (Catarine da Costa) was found wrapped in a plastic sheet and half hidden under a sports pavilion in a football field on the outskirts of Stockholm. It had been cut up and the pieces neatly tied together. Once the police had concluded their on-the-spot investigation, the body parts were taken to the morgue in Stockholm and subsequently examined by the police pathologist Dr Haerm. His opinion was that the dissection had been done by an expert, probably a butcher. He claimed that he would know more once he had put the body back together again. Within a few days the police conducted a massive search of the area, concentrating on butchers' shops and gun owners who were known hunters and would be familiar with dissection techniques. They drew a blank. Ten days later another body turned up in a public place. Once again, the body was delivered to the laboratory of Dr Haerm. The police waited impatiently for his report. He confirmed that the woman had been strangled and opined that the murder was committed by the same

person that killed da Costa. He also said that, on further examination, he had discarded the idea that the murderer might be a butcher. From the way that the body had been mutilated, it was obviously the work of someone with a background of operating on human bodies, probably a surgeon. Haerm was pulling an enormous double bluff. As the medical advisor to the police he was expected to be able to point them in the direction that clues from the corpse showed. If he continued to maintain that the dissection was the work of a butcher, one of his colleagues might decide to speak his piece and say that it was the obvious work of a surgeon. This would call into doubt his own authority and might even set the police wondering why he hadn't vouchsafed the information himself. The thought that the murderer might be a surgeon lifted the murder of a common prostitute into another stratum. The newspapers picked up on it and the prospect of a Dr Jekyll and Mr Hyde on the loose sent a shiver down the spine of the Swedish public. Then, in quick succession, six more prostitutes were found murdered in Stockholm's red-light district. Now the newspapers were hysterically vying with each other to produce the most lurid headlines. The similarity with the Whitechapel killings of Jack the Ripper 100 years previously figured heavily in the editor's art. Extra police were put on the streets and prostitutes were warned of the danger they faced going off with punters they didn't know. It was hardly necessary to warn the working girls. They were always aware of the dangers they faced. But they had to earn a living and they realised that the police might be pests but they were the best bet they had to secure their safety. They co-operated wholeheartedly. From the dozens of statements taken the police began to build up a profile of the man they wanted. Meanwhile, Dr Haerm continued to examine the string of bodies delivered to his post mortem table and give the police all the information he could gather, safe in the knowledge that he would be the last one they would suspect. Killing and dissecting the bodies and then having the pleasure of putting them back together again was like a drug. He was aware that each time he took to the streets he was exposing himself to danger but this added to the thrill. His method was simple. He drove through the areas where the hookers operated late in the evening. When he came across a loner peddling her trade, he claimed he was in the mood to party and took her back to his house and ran the car into the garage. At the house another doctor, Lars Thomas, was waiting. Thomas was a colleague of Haerm. Haerm had convinced him that he was on a sacred mission. Haerm claimed to be the High Priest of a Druid sect dedicated to cleansing the world of the carriers of plague and disease – the spawn of the devil – the prostitute. As evidence he cited the widespread disease of Aids that had so recently been visited not only on Sweden but every country of the world. Although it was regarded as a male homosexual disease, Haerm convinced Thomas that this was government propaganda to conceal the real facts – that promiscuous sex was the culprit. Whether Dr Thomas really believed this or was just going along for the sexual pleasure of a little necrophilia and cannibalism is not known. As soon as the garage door closed Haerm would lead the girl into the house where Thomas was waiting. They would grab the woman, strangle her and strip the body. While the body was still warm, they would make love to it and play-act games around the house. When the body had cooled and the blood congealed,

they carried it out to the garage and carefully dissected it. Often they would take a piece and cook it. Haerm explained to the receptive Thomas that this was an essential part of the cleansing ritual that the priesthood had observed for thousands of years. For validation he claimed that the Aztecs were the founding fathers of Druidism and they had realised the efficacy of bonding with a higher being through the blood and flesh of those sacrificed.

The police were clueless. The prostitutes were more than happy to help the police out in any way they could. Several of them recalled a youngish looking man who patrolled the streets late at night in a white Volkswagen but never seemed to stop. They put him down as a nervous punter who couldn't get up the courage to stop or a pervert who got a thrill just looking at the girls. Then a significant piece of information dropped on to the desk of the detective in charge of the case. One of the girls remembered part of the number plate of the midnight cruiser in the white Volkswagen. It didn't take the police long to come up with a short list of suspects. And top of the list was Dr Haerm. He snugly fitted the profile he had given the police himself.

The police boned up on Haerm's medical career and drew a blank. He had written a few tracts in the medical press about such things as strangulation and its use to heighten the sensation of sexual intercourse. He had also written several papers on the forensic dissection of cadavers and the clues that could be found from various procedures. But he was one of the foremost forensic scientists in the country and it was the sort of article he would be expected to write. The police decided that they had enough to suggest that Haerm should be interviewed and asked him to pop into the station for a chat when he had a moment. If the doctor had a momentary fear that he had been discovered, he didn't show it. He turned up in the late afternoon and, after joking with the detectives he worked with, agreed to be questioned.

He found the whole affair mildly amusing. When questioned about the report that his car had been seen cruising the red-light district, he claimed that he had been fascinated by the number of bodies of prostitutes that had passed through his hands and wanted to know something about their working environment so that he had a fuller understanding of what was going on. It seemed a reasonable answer and as there was no forensic evidence to contradict what he claimed, he was released. As he had now become a part of the enquiry a request by the police for him to be suspended from the pathology department was granted.

The police were uneasy with Haerm's reasonable explanation and ran an investigation into his background. They found that he had been recently widowed. His wife had committed suicide but as far as the police were concerned there were no suspicious circumstances surrounding her death. The couple were devoted to each other and friends were adamant that there was no undercurrent of strife between them. They also mentioned that Haerm had dropped out a little since his wife's death. He seemed to spend all his time working and had little time for friends to whom he had previously been close.

Haerm was no fool. He realised that now the police had got his name in the frame, they would keep a close eye on him and be ready to pounce at the slightest indication that he was up to something he shouldn't be. They had come to the house and given it a cursory search. The most damning evidence they had come up with was a post mortem photograph of his wife with a rope around her neck. Haerm had managed to explain that away easily. It was a photograph taken in the morgue by a colleague. He didn't like the idea of it lying around for everyone to see so had taken it with the intention of destroying it. The picture had been put aside and he had forgotten all about it. Haerm was afraid that the detectives might decide to come back for a closer look, so he

roped in Thomas and they spent a couple of days cleaning the house. Both doctors were well aware of the difficulty of completely destroying the evidence of their crimes but they did the best they could. Just when they were beginning to feel safe, three bodies that they thought they had successfully hidden turned up. This gave a fillip to the police enquiry that had been getting nowhere and under the rod from both the press and the government. But once again they were disappointed. Although all three bodies bore the distinctive stamp of the serial killer, they delivered no extra clues. Once more the detectives saw the case drifting away from them. The breakthrough came from a completely unexpected quarter. A school teacher reported to a social worker that she suspected that one of her pupils had been sexually molested. The social worker found out that the girl was the daughter of a doctor with whom she often had professional dealings. At first she assumed that the girl was either lying or was mistaken. Perhaps the doctor had examined her for some suspected illness and the child had become confused? She called Dr Thomas. Thomas at first denied all knowledge of what his four-year-old daughter was accusing him. His wife backed him up. The social worker became uneasy with the situation and called in the police. By this time his wife had rethought the position. When the police arrived, she said that her husband wished to make a statement. She sat in the corner of the room sobbing quietly as Thomas admitted that he had been responsible for the molestation of his daughter. Once he started to confess he couldn't stop. The dumbstruck police had trouble keeping their notes as he blabbed out his part in the murder of the prostitutes and implicated Dr Haerm as well. This time the police didn't pussy-foot around. Before the arrest of Dr Thomas became public knowledge, they had charged Haerm with the murders of eight women, Annica Mors, Catarine da Costa, Kristine Cravache, Lena Grans, Cate Falk, Lena Manson,

Lota Svenson, Tazuga Toyonaga and his wife Ann-Catrine. The body of Lena Bofors was not recovered but was considered to have suffered the same fate as the others. Haerm accepted it all and claimed that he had been suffering from an untreated psychiatric problem for some time. He was examined by a board of psychiatrists who came to the conclusion that, although he was delusional, he was competent to stand trial. Dr Thomas was arraigned on the charge of rape and murder of Catarine da Costa and being an accessory after the fact in the cases of the others. He was also charged with performing an incestuous act with his daughter. In September 1988 both were found guilty and given life sentences.

10
John Christie

Notting Hill may have become fashionable in the past few years but when Christie lived in Rillington Place in Notting Hill Gate, it was anything but. Even if it had been, the sickening crimes that he committed there would have initiated a bottomless dive in house prices immediately. Christie was the mild-mannered man that would have made Clarke Kent, Superman's alter ego, look positively butch. Bald, of medium height, a weak, paunchy body and milk bottle-bottomed glasses, he looked like what he always thought of himself as – a loser. He put most of his misery down to his father, a carpenter and a tyrannical martinet of a man. At school, in Boothstown, Yorkshire, it was natural for Christie Jr to be bullied. He was habitually called 'four eyes' and made the victim of any horseplay that occurred in the school yard. At the first opportunity, he left school and found a job in the hope that he would have a better chance of being accepted in the adult world. This was not to be. In some respects the persecution became worse. Especially after he was led on by one of the women where he worked but was unable to make love to her when the opportunity arose. The girl took great delight in telling everyone who would listen that Christie couldn't 'do it'. To try to get sympathy he invented illnesses. Instead of making people feel sorry for him, they lost even more respect when he constantly snivelled about his weaknesses. This pushed him into claiming even more life-threatening problems and before long, he talked himself into an unhealthy dose of hypochondria – a condition that was to stay with him for the rest of his life.

In 1915, when he was barely 17, in spite of his awful eyesight and general weakness, he was inducted into the armed forces and immediately committed to the trenches in France. In the unhealthy, unsanitary conditions he was constantly ill but he got no sympathy from his superiors or from the other recruits who shared the same conditions and often the same illnesses. This was brought on by poor food, stress and the appalling conditions in the trenches – from which there was no relief. It was a God-send when a shell landed in his trench and he was blown out into the open. He laid there for hours before being discovered and carried back to the hospital. At some time during his spell in the open he got a dose of mustard gas. It was mild but enough to make his weak eyes even worse. The trauma of being blown up left him blind for three months. Although at first sympathetic, the doctor finally got tired of his constant whining and suggested that his blindness wasn't the effect of the explosion and gas but an attempt to work his ticket. It was a harsh judgment. When he was examined, the specialist reported that he was blind but in his opinion this was brought on by hysteria. Invalided out of the Army, he got himself a job with the Halifax Police Force as a civilian clerical worker. He liked that. He always told anyone who would listen that he was with the police – plain-clothed. This didn't last long. Some articles went missing from the changing room and were traced back to Christie. He escaped prosecution because the police thought that taking him to court and having to explain their carelessness in putting temptation in his way would make them look silly. He took a job with the post office and for a while seemed to settle down. He was still mortally afraid of his domineering father and when he was prosecuted for stealing from the post office, rather than face him, he went to live in London. The Twenties were not a good time for finding work. His lack of charm and a thick regional accent didn't help. He bummed around doing whatever jobs cropped up or a little petty pilfering. Doing casual work as a part-time baker's delivery boy, he met the woman who would eventually become his wife – and murder victim. Ethel was a physically tough but emotionally fragile woman. She had little experience of men and Christie suited her. He was quiet and easily dominated. She wasn't too keen on the sexual side of married life. She had been brought up to believe that sort of thing was dirty and not something that a 'nice' girl would indulge in. It was two years before she allowed Christie to do 'it' and it was disastrous from both their perspectives. Living from hand to mouth without even the prospect of a bit of hanky-panky under the blankets, their marriage began to fall apart. It hadn't far to fall. In 1923, Ethel declared that she had had enough and went home to mum. This brought on another of Christie's attacks of hysteria and he completely lost his voice for a while. Deserted by his wife, Christie decided that he had nothing to lose and took a desperate gamble. He hung out in Battersea, approaching manufacturing firms and banks claiming to be a wealthy man interested in revitalising his fortune with an investment plan that would make anyone who came in with him rich. Mostly he was shown the door but there were just enough dupes who listened and lent him money to run him into trouble. With his world threatening once again to implode on him, he got into an argument with one of the women he had borrowed money from, lost control and hit her over the head with a cricket bat. Again, he was in trouble with the police. A short custodial sentence was handed down and Christie was out of harm's way for a few months. When back on the streets, he went to see his estranged wife and somehow managed to talk her into

returning to their marital home. The reunion seemed to steady him and he worked for a year in a public house in Brixton. Then, one foggy night when he was returning home after closing time, he stepped off the pavement without looking and was mown down by a lorry. It was not all bad luck. He suffered injuries to his head, arm, collar-bone and leg and was laid up for a month. But it did get him an introduction to the company whose truck had hit him. And the offer of a job. Older and wiser now, he tried hard to be a good employee. It lasted until 1940.

The Second World War began and everyone's priorities changed or were changed for them. Christie's job with the trucking company went but he applied to the police force for a job as a Reserve Police Constable, citing his work with the Halifax Police as his credential. London was chaotic at this time and there was no time to check the CV of a man who was volunteering to put himself at risk on the streets of a city which expected to bear the brunt of the enemy's Air Force at any moment. Christie loved the job. For the first time in his life he had some authority and he never lost an opportunity to exercise it. He liked nothing better than to bully and even to prosecute anyone who flaunted the stringent blackout rules by showing the smallest chinks of light. He became so overbearing that Ethel once again decided she needed a break from his continuous boasting about his exploits on the streets and set off for Sheffield to visit her family. Left on his own, in daily fear of his life from the bombs that rained down on the city, Christie began to look around for some companionship. Ruth Fuerst was not a happy woman. She had come to England with her parents before the war but her thick Austrian accent and the bombs nightly killing hundreds in the city did not sit well with those around her. At first she had tried to explain that the reason her parents had come to London was because they did not like what was happening to their homeland. Nobody listened. Then one night she met Christie in an air raid shelter. He was sympathetic and listen to her tales of woe. He didn't laugh at her accent or be hurtful about her nationality. When she met him again a few days later, she was happy to be invited to his house. Christie was excited by the prospect of the unknown woman in the house alone with him. In these circumstances most lonely men would have used their influence as a Reserve Constable to buy a little something extra from 'under the counter', maybe a bottle of plonk and, if he really wanted to push the boat out, have a bath. John Christie's idea of foreplay was to dig a deep hole in the garden. Ruth was grateful to Christie for showing her a little kindness in a hostile world and when he moved in on her, after they had eaten the sandwiches he had prepared, she didn't object. Christie was a clumsy, inexperienced lover and the union was not going well. He suddenly seized the frustrated girl by the throat and didn't let go until he had throttled her. He sat back and studied his handiwork for a few minutes. An urge to have sex with the pliant, uncomplicated body surged through him. He tried to control himself but the urge was too strong. It was the first time he had known total sexual satisfaction. He would have liked to keep the body for further gratification at a later date but he was afraid that it might be discovered if his wife unexpectedly returned. He buried Ruth's body in the back garden and then waited for his crime to be discovered. Nothing happened. No one seemed worried by the disappearance of a lonely Austrian girl in the midst of one of the most sustained periods of enemy bombing of the entire war.

Christie was terrified that Ruth would be missed and she would have told someone that she was coming to see him. But he need not have worried. He was the only friend the poor girl had. Later that year he got a job in a factory making radio components in Park Royal. There, he became friendly with a girl called Muriel Eady. During a conversation he learned that Muriel was expecting and wasn't happy with the situation. Christie told her that he had worked with hospitals during the war and had learned a lot about surgery. Enough to be able to help out quite a few girls in her position. At first

she was reluctant but Christie gradually managed to overcome her natural resistance to making her body hostage to Christie's unusual expertise. To reassure Muriel, Christie had promised her that his wife would be with her while he performed the simple operation. He didn't think it worth telling her that they would now be alone in the house. Instead, he took the advantage of having an empty house to prepare for the 'operation'. This amounted to clearing off the kitchen table, covering it with an oilcloth – and digging another hole in the garden. Muriel arrived spot on time, eager to get the whole sordid business over and done with. Christie made her a cup of tea, apologised for his wife's absence but assured her that she would be joining them at any moment. He then explained the procedure. He got her to remove her undergarments and told her about the beneficial effects of gas. Muriel wasn't happy about the gas bit, nor the fact that Mrs Christie hadn't appeared. Christie explained his side of the business and persuaded her that it was as much for his benefit as hers. He got her to sit with the wet towel over her head over the gas ring and waited. After a while she got drowsy and Christie helped her on to the table. Swiftly, he divested her of the rest of her clothes and ran excited hands over her bare body. The effects of the gas began to wear off and she became aware of what Christie was doing. It wasn't performing an abortion. She struggled to sit up but Christie held her down, talking to her all the time, trying to convince her that it was all part of the procedure. Muriel's continued efforts to get free snapped Christie's fragile control. He gripped her around the neck and hung on until she was dead. Once she stopped moving, he fell on the body and had violent intercourse with it. Sated, he wrapped the oilcloth around her and dragged her to the back door. Before dropping her into her unconsecrated grave, he got an old tobacco tin and a pair of scissors and took a trophy: a tuft of pubic hair. Satisfied that everything was as it should be, he dropped the body into the hole, backfilled it and went to bed. For a while Christie worried that

John Christie arrested for the murder of his wife and prostitutes that he lured to his house in Notting Hill Gate. (Popperfoto)

someone at the radio factory might connect him with Muriel and come looking for him. When no police came, it confirmed what Christie had always thought – he was too smart for them.

The war ended, Ethel returned to Notting Hill Gate and husband and wife settled down to what passed for domestic bliss in the run-down house with a dreadful secret buried in the garden. Reconstructing the city after five years of bombing and neglect meant plenty of work for everyone and Mr and Mrs Christie were able to keep in work without much trouble. As an added source of income they had lodgers – Mr and Mrs Evans, John and Beryl, and their baby daughter Geraldine. Christie quite liked Evans. Evans was a simple soul, easily impressed with Christie's stories of derring-do in two world wars. Evans was a truck driver and was often away from home. Ethel was also out of the house a lot and Christie and Mrs Evans became quite friendly. Beryl found coping with the baby by herself was a burden and Christie would look after Geraldine whenever Beryl fancied popping out for an hour or two. She told Christie that she was expecting another baby and was terrified of another mouth to feed. She asked Christie if he knew anyone who could help her. Christie instantly claimed to have the necessary skill and would be happy to put it at her disposal at the next opportunity. A few days later John Evans went off to deliver a load in Wales, Ethel went out to visit a friend and the house was set up for a gynaecological operation – John Christie style. He called Beryl down to the kitchen and gave her a glass of red wine. He then suggested that she put a wetted towel over her head and sat by the stove with her head over the gas ring. She wasn't too happy about this but Christie assured her that he had done many operations like this and the gas would just make her drowsy so that he could operate without causing her pain. She tried again but got frightened and abandoned the idea. Christie was sympathetic and tried to coax her into going ahead with the abortion but she had changed her mind. Christie was overheated now and wanted satisfaction. He grabbed her

by the neck and wrestled her to the floor. Beryl tried to resist but he was like a madman. By the time he had gained control of himself, he had another corpse on his hands. With the naked body of the dead woman at his feet Christie now had the familiar urge to have intercourse with the corpse. He frantically made love to the body then sat beside it and finished off the glass of wine that Beryl never did. In the bedroom the baby was screaming its head off for its mother. Christie panicked. At any moment his wife could return to find a dead body in her kitchen and a disturbed baby in the bedroom. This time he had no carefully prepared hole to drop the body in. But first he had to do something about the baby. He stopped by the side of the drawer that had been made into a makeshift crib. He thought of simply shutting the drawer. This would reduce the sound of the screams but it wasn't a solution to the problem. Mercilessly, Christie took the tiny neck of the baby in his hands and squeezed until the crying stopped and the body went limp. His action hadn't solved his problems. Now he had two bodies to deal with. As a temporary measure he wrapped the bodies of mother and child and hid them in the wash house at the rear of the building. Later, he would find somewhere more permanent to hide them. At that moment the front door opened and John Evans walked in. Christie hastily revised his plans. He told Evans that he had come back from work and found Beryl had killed the baby and then gassed herself. He had thought that Evans had done it after the quarrel he had heard them having the night before and had hidden the bodies in the wash house. Evans swore that he knew nothing about it and Christie assured him that he believed what he said. But… would the police? He suggested to Evans that he went off and kept out of the way to give him, Christie, time to work something out. He reminded the simple-minded Evans that he had been a Police Constable and knew how to fix these things. Evans expressed gratitude and promised to leave the next morning. Early the following day he went out and sold what things he could carry from the flat and then disappeared. Christie waited

CLOSING CITY PRICES

RING CUN 5141 FOR
ROOTES
CAR HIRE

Evening Standard

40,107 WEDNESDAY, APRIL 22, 1953 ●●Three-halfpence

FINAL NIGHT EXTRA

MeKay SHIRTS
MEKAY, LONDON, N.W.I

Case against Christie revealed

'THREE WOMEN GASSED AND STRANGLED'

His alleged story of struggles

'I MUST HAVE GONE HAYWIRE'

Evening Standard Reporter

The prosecution at Clerkenwell to-day alleged that John Reginald Halliday Christie asphyxiated his wife and murdered three girls by strangulation and carbon monoxide poisoning.

A statement Christie is alleged to have made was read in court. It described how he put his wife "to sleep" and how the three girls died after each had started fighting him.

In one part of the statement Christie is alleged to have said, "I must have gone haywire."

Christie, a 54-year-old transport clerk, is accused of murdering his wife, Ethel (aged 54), Rita Elizabeth Nelson (24), Kathleen Maloney (25) and Hectorina McKay McLennan (25), at his flat at 10, Rillington Place, Notting Hill.

TWO SKELETONS

Chief Inspector Percy Law, head of Scotland Yard's photographers, told the court he had photographed the bodies of the three girls and also two re-constructed skeletons, one without a skull. They were built from bones found in the garden.

Mr. John F. Claxton, for the Director of Public Prosecutions, said that Mrs. Christie's body was found buried under floorboards at the Rillington Place flat. The three girls were found in a coal cupboard over which wallpaper had been fastened.

There was evidence of sexual interference with each of the three girls after death.

Mr. Claxton said that when P-c Ledger saw Christie on the embankment near Putney Bridge on March 31. Christie gave the wrong name.

In a police van on the way to the police station Christie threw across to the officer his identity card, which disclosed his true name and address.

At the police station he was told that four bodies had been found, one of which was apparently that of his wife. Christie started to cry, and said: "She woke me up, she was choking. I could not stand it any longer. I could not bear to see her suffer."

'Persecution'

Then, said Mr. Claxton, he made the statement which said:

● "My wife had been suffering a great deal from persecution and assaults. She got very depressed.

"On December 14 I was awakened about 8.15 a.m. I think, by my wife moving about. I sat up and saw that she appeared to be convulsive. Her face was blue and she was choking. I did what I could to try to restore

breathing, but it was hopeless.

"I got a stocking and tied it round her neck to put her to sleep. I got out of bed and saw a small bottle and cup on a table. I noticed that the bottle contained two phenobarbitone tablets, and it originally contained 25. I knew then she must have taken the remainder."

'I was in a state'

In the alleged statement Christie said he left his wife's body in bed for two or three days. Then he half-carried, half-dragged her to the front room, put her in a depression under the floorboards and covered her with earth.

"I was in a state," the statement continued, "and I did not know what to do. After Christmas I sold my furniture. I made up a bed in the back room.

"I got 37s. for my wife's ring. I took it off her finger for a keepsake, but sold it as I was hard up and had to get food."

Mr. Claxton then read the remainder of the alleged statement. It fell into three

sections, each section dealing with one of the girls.

The section dealing with MALONEY said that one evening when he had gone out he met a drunken woman on the way back who stood in front of him and demanded £1.

In the statement Christie alleged that she followed him to his house, and he said: "I went to the kitchen. She picked up a frying pan and hit me.

"I closed with her and there was a struggle and she fell back against a chair. There was a piece of rope on the chair.

"I do not remember what happened. I must have gone haywire.

"I got, but not very suspecting. She was still in the chair. I pulled away a cupboard to gain access to a small alcove. I must have put her in there."

One came

Of RITA NELSON, Christie said in his alleged statement that he met her in a café in Notting Hill Gate. He mentioned he was leaving his flat, and she suggested that she should come round to see it.

"She mentioned something about Irish blood, I remember she started fighting. I am very quiet and avoid fighting. She was on the floor. I must have put her in the s'cove."

'She started struggling'

Then came HECTORINA McLENNAN. Christie alleged that she returned to his flat alone after being there earlier with a man.

The alleged statement said "She was very funny about it. She started struggling like anything and some of her clothing got torn.

"She then sort of fell limp as I had hold of her.

"I pulled the cupboard away again, and I must have put her in there."

Gas light

One witness this afternoon, Mrs. Mary Riley, of Clydesdale Road, Notting Hill, said that in March she paid Christie £7 13s. advance rent for his flat at Rillington Place.

She said there was gas light and a gas oven in the kitchen, but in the bedroom they had to use candle light.

In the kitchen there was "a very unpleasant smell."

Late this afternoon Miss Maureen Mary Anne Riggs broke down and cried as she said she introduced Kathleen Maloney to Christie in an Edgware Road bar.

Full report begins on Page THREE.

JOHN REGINALD HALLIDAY CHRISTIE.
His alleged statement said: "I could not bear to see my wife suffer."

West End crowd chase jewel shop bandit

Evening Standard Reporter

The manager of a jeweller's shop in Great Portland Street, Marylebone, struggled with a bandit in the shop to-day — then the bandit escaped and was chased along the street by a large crowd headed by a policeman.

As the constable was about to pounce, the bandit flung a raincoat in his face and got away.

Mr. Cyril Page, the manager, was in the shop of Thomas A. Robinson and Company when a man aged about 26 walked in and was shown some rings.

"Suddenly," said Mr. Page, "he hit me on the chin.

"I know a bit about boxing and hit him back. The man broke away after a struggle."

70 degrees at the seaside

The temperature at Bournemouth this afternoon reached 70 degrees.

This was the highest since September.

In London it was 62. The Air Ministry forecast that the warm spell will continue to-morrow.

WEATHER—Fine

Forecast for to-morrow: Moderate E. winds; cloud at first, becoming fine; warm in afternoon. Further outlook: Dry and fine.

Lighting-up time (London) 9.7 p.m.

TELEPHONE: CENTRAL 3000

430 MAU MAU SHOT TRYING TO GET AWAY

Four hundred and thirty Mau Mau terrorists in Kenya have been shot in the last six months, while resisting arrest or trying to escape, Mr. Oliver Lyttelton, Colonial Secretary, told the Commons to-day.

Home Guards had killed 47 Mau Mau.

Mr. Lyttelton said he had given an assurance that every measure would be taken to prevent indiscriminate shooting.

7 from Korea arrive home

Evening Standard Reporter

ABINGDON AIRFIELD, Berks, Wednesday. — The Royal Air Force Hastings aircraft bringing seven men freed from North Korean prison camps landed here this afternoon.

They were six British civilians and an Irish missionary who had been interned in North Korea for nearly three years.

As the airplane taxied to a halt, Mr. R. H. Scott, assistant Under-Secretary at the Foreign Office, went on board to welcome the seven internees.

They are Captain Vyvyan Holt, who was British Minister in Seoul when the Korean war broke out; Bishop Alfred Cooper, Anglican missionary; Commissioner Herbert Lord of the Salvation Army; Mr. George Blake, British Vice-consul in Seoul; Mr. Norman Owen, First Secretary of the British Legation in Seoul; Mr. Philip Deane of the Observer newspaper; and the Rev. Thomas Quinlan, Irish missionary.

From Berlin

Relatives and friends clapped and cheered as the men walked down the gangway.

After going through the Customs the men were taken to the officers' mess for tea.

The seven were freed by the North Koreans as a result of Russian intervention. They were taken to Moscow by train, then flew on to Berlin.

They had flown from Berlin in two hours, 18 minutes.

until he had gone then told Ethel about finding Mrs Evans body. She told him to call the police. This he did. He was so convincing that when they left they didn't consider looking elsewhere for the murderer. Evans was in the frame and that was good enough for them. It only got better when John Evans walked into the police station in Merthyr Tydfil. He explained that he had found his wife dead when he returned home, had panicked and tried to hide the body. It wasn't good enough. Christie had already given them a scenario they could live with and they didn't want to have to start the investigation all over again. After spending a few hours talking to the police, Evans suddenly remembered that he had murdered his wife and child and signed a confession to that effect. At his trial he retracted his confession and blamed Christie. But the damage had been done and when John and Ethel Christie were in the witness box, they told a tale that left the jury no recourse but to return a guilty verdict. John Evans, still protesting his innocence, was executed in Pentonville Prison on 9 March 1950. Christie laid low for a while after the close call of the police investigation. As time went by and his relationship with his wife deteriorated even more, he began to work out ways to satisfy his necrophilic fancies. His success rate with women was not good. So he began to check out the possibilities of getting street-walkers back to his house. It would have to be at a time when his wife was out but this did not present much of a problem. She was out more than she was in. Getting the girls was easier than he expected. They had no problem in accompanying the little man. It was better than plying their trade in the damp bushes or up a draughty alley and there might even be a chance of picking up a trinket or two in the house. Christie had already prepared his house for the next act. There was a sizeable cupboard under the stairs with a door into the kitchen. It suited his purpose. It hadn't been used regularly since they moved in. It harboured a few bits of dust-covered broken furniture and a box or two but that was all. He picked up Rita Nelson outside the cinema. It was a cold night and she was glad of the chance to get off the streets for a while. Christie explained that he was a retired police officer and recently widowed. At the house he offered her a drink which she gratefully accepted. And several more. It wasn't long before the warmth of the house and the alcohol made her feel drowsy. Christie suggested that she removed her coat and moved in behind her. Without warning he struck the unsuspecting woman across the back of the head with a rolling pin he had left handy for just that purpose. As she sagged forward on to her knees, stunned, he leapt onto her and tied one of his wife's stockings around her neck. She was able to offer little resistance and in a very short time Christie had another victim on which to practice his necromancy. He went through the routine that was now becoming familiar to him. He stripped the body and had intercourse with it before dragging it into the cupboard and covering it up with the bits and pieces already in there.

His next victim was Kathleen Mahoney. She was also glad of an off-street romance and had no qualms about following her punter to his nearby home. Christie had thought about his new victim. He wanted to cut out the brutality of his past killings and try something a little more refined. He bought a free-standing gas ring and a length of rubber hosing. Above a deck chair he fitted a sort of low-level canopy. When he had plied Kathleen with enough drink to overcome any sense of caution she might be harbouring, Christie introduced her to the chair. He explained that it was a sort of throne. Giggling, she let Christie help her into it and arrange the canopy over her head. He then opened the valve on the gas ring and watched as the girl was gradually overcome by the fumes and sank into unconsciousness. He quickly dispatched her with his trusty stocking, raped the cooling body and placed it in the cupboard under the stairs before his wife returned. He struck once more using the same technique. Hectorina McLennan was his last victim. When he killed each of the prostitutes, he cut off and preserved a tuft of pubic hair. When Hectorina went missing, the police started inquiring into the disappearance of the other prostitutes, all from the same area, all within a relatively short space of time. It was enough. He would wait until the missing prostitutes were forgotten before inviting anyone home again.

Then the unthinkable happened. The thing for which he was not prepared. The event that has undone so many killers before him. The bodies in the cupboard were discovered. A smell had been building in the kitchen for some time. If John and Ethel had been on speaking terms, Christie could possibly have headed off any suggestion of a search to find the cause. Ethel returned one evening from work. The smell in the kitchen was pretty ripe so she decided to investigate. It didn't take her long to discover the three bodies in the cupboard. Before she could decide what to do about it, Christie came home. When she tackled him on the subject he at first denied all knowledge of the bodies, then shifted his argument and claimed that the women had been murdered by Evans. It was a weak argument. The police had searched the entire house after the discovery of Beryl Evans body and could hardly have missed the remains of the prostitutes in the cupboard. Ethel wanted to go to the police there and then but he managed to talk her out of it. He waited until she had calmed down a little and then attacked. He strangled her with her own stocking. This was one body he had no necrophilic feeling for. He needed to find a hiding place for the body, and fast. The garden and the cupboard were full. He found a loose floorboard leading into the kitchen and levered it up. Underneath was a space of about 18 inches. He levered up the other boards and dropped the body of his late wife into the space. He hammered the boards back in place and stood and considered his position. This was serious. It wasn't another friendless girl or common prostitute lying under the floorboards, it was his wife. And she had a family and friends. Just a few days previously her father had come to pay her a visit. Doubtless she would have told him about their strained relationship. Then there were the friends she

was always going to the cinema with or visiting. They would probably come inquiring and he had to have a story ready to put them off the scent. But first he had to try to cover his tracks. The carpet over the floorboards was enough to disguise the resting place of his wife. He went out and bought a large sheet of plywood, a roll of heavy-duty wallpaper, a packet of paste and a brush. He nailed the plywood across the door to the cupboard and then pasted the wallpaper over it. It wasn't a complete solution to his problems but it would have to do. When anyone inquired about his wife he told them whatever he thought would put them off the scent. The house of death and putrefaction began to work on his mind. He gave up work and supported himself by selling bits and pieces of furniture, his wife's gold wedding ring and clothes – anything that would keep him going until he could find a long-term solution to his problems. But the bodies in the house began to haunt him. Everyday he went out and wandered the streets. Finally, he could stand it no longer. He had to make a break. First, he redecorated the kitchen, making sure that there was no hint of the cupboard holding the damning secrets behind the painted wallpaper. Then, he found an Irish family and sublet the flat to them. He now became a bit of a nomad, dossing down where he could, getting by on what he could steal or beg.

The head leaseholder on 10 Rillington Place heard about the subletting and straightaway evicted the new tenants. Mr Beresford Brown, the owner of the building, decided to move in himself. He was soon to have a terrible shock. Attempting to drive a nail into the kitchen wall he discovered that it was hollow. He quickly stripped away the paper and plywood and discovered – three decaying corpses. When he recovered, he sent for the police. A search of the house revealed the remains of Ethel and that made the detectives decide that a search of the garden should be undertaken. It didn't take long to discover the two bodies buried there. The hole had been too shallow and bones had worked themselves to the surface. It was enough to get the police started on a nationwide search for the missing tenant, John Christie. It didn't take long for the press to pick up on the connection with that other murder of only a few short years before. Straightaway they suggested that there had been a grave miscarriage of justice and that the man, John Evans, who had been sent to the scaffold only a couple of years earlier, might have been telling the truth when he tried to implicate Christie in the death of his wife and daughter.

John Christie was found standing on Putney Bridge, staring into the Thames, by an off-duty policeman. He made no attempt to resist arrest and when he was taken to Putney Police Station and charged he made a full confession. When questioned, he gave a murder-by-murder account of how he killed each of his victims and detailed description of what he had done to the dead bodies. Now that they had the murderer and his confession, the police quickly gathered forensic evidence to back up his words. The only item that was still outstanding was that John Evans had been hanged for a crime he didn't commit. Christie was not helpful on this point. At one time he appeared to admit that he had strangled Mrs Evans – but at her own request. She told him, he said, that she was desperately unhappy and had made several unsuccessful attempts to take her own life before appealing to him to help her out. The baby, Geraldine Evans, he strenuously denied killing and laid the blame on the executed Evans. The jury didn't really care by this stage. They had sat through so much horrifyingly graphic evidence that all they wanted to do was get the trial over and go about their own lives. Christie was found guilty and sentenced to death. He was hanged on the same scaffold in Pentonville Prison that had been used, just over three years earlier, for the man who had been convicted on evidence Christie had given in court. To this day there is widely diverse opinion about what really happened in 10 Rillington Place. It's all gone now. Not even the name remains. But the memories of what happened there all those years ago are as fresh as ever.

11
Edmund Kemper

Edmund Kemper could have made a killing as a monster in B movies. He was six feet nine inches tall and weighed in at 20 stone. He was reasonably good looking with wide eyes 'that made you shiver', as one of the witnesses at his trial stated. It was a pity he never got a shot at the movies, he might have sublimated his sadistic urges with celluloid violence and fake blood. Or he might have taken the opportunity to exploit his fame and become even more of a monster – if that were possible. Not all actors have the ability to turn into a sweet old man with a loving family when they are off the set like Boris Karloff and Peter Cushing. Kemper was huge at birth, over 13lb, and steadily grew bigger. By the age of four, he was already a head taller than any of his contemporaries. And strong with it. He led a lonely childhood. His strength and lack of control assured that he had no playmates and even his sister had reason to hate him. Without the discipline of other children, he was left to find his own amusement. His sister soon learned to keep out of his way so he vented his loneliness and frustration on her dolls. When that became boring he turned his attention to animals. He found amusement in lighting a small fire and holding a tin of ants over the flame. When he found a cat in his garden, he tied a rag dipped in paraffin to its tail and set light to it. He found the poor demented creature's efforts to outrun the flame exciting and highly amusing. When the cat died, he cut off its head and kept it in a plastic bag until it was discovered by his teacher. He was disciplined for

bringing the head to school but nobody seemed to think the youngster might be in need of more than a dressing down by the head or a demerit. By the time he left school he was six feet six inches and still growing. And completely out of control. There were very few people around ready to take on the youth with a history of viciousness and an established hate of authority. His mother, Clarnell, was terrified of him. Only his sister could get anywhere with him and even her control did not extend to getting him to do anything he didn't want to. In desperation, his mother spoke to her father. He was an ex-Air Force Sergeant and assured her that all the boy needed was a little discipline. It was agreed that Edmund should be sent to live with the grandparents. As first, the union of young and old seemed to work. He wasn't too keen on his grandfather who was a bit overbearing and determined to prove his point to his daughter. The rapport between grandmother and boy seemed much stronger. As Edmund settled in and his surroundings became more familiar, his true feelings began to show. He was avoided by the local youths who would taunt him about his size and suggest that he was impotent. But always when they were well out of harm's way. He tried to get friendly with one of the daughters of the next-door neighbour. She was quite friendly when he first moved in but altered her attitude when she saw how the rest of her classmates treated him. She didn't want to be the odd one out, so she made up for her earlier friendliness by being one of his worst taunters. He didn't have the personality to turn the other cheek. It was just his neighbour's luck to run into him when she was on her own with no possibility of escape. He tried to reason with her but instead of retracting what she had previously said, fear caused her to repeat her jibes. Edmund grabbed her and tried to rape her. She managed to break free and ran screaming into the house. The police turned up ten minutes later. They were not unsympathetic. Edmund told them simply what had happened. As the girl had not been hurt or seriously interfered with, they gave Edmund a warning and left. Another opportunity to give the oversized teenager a helping hand lost. His grandfather was outraged and tried to impose a ban on Edmund's external activities. It was a hopeless task. He was just not strong enough nor had the mental authority to force him to shape up. Even his grandmother began to turn against him.

The constant griping that he had to put up with from his grandparents couldn't go on. He borrowed a rifle off a local garage owner where he occasionally worked to earn a few dollars, and went home to confront his grandparents. He found his grandmother in the kitchen. She was intent on preparing a meal and didn't hear him as he walked up to her and shot her in the back of the head. She fell to the floor. He bent over her. She was moaning and trying to sit up. Kemper pumped two more shots into her and crouched beside her and watched her die. His grandfather was working on his car in the garage, he glanced up and asked Kemper what he wanted. For an answer Kemper shot him dead. Excited by what he had done, he kicked his grandfather's body before returning to the house and drinking a bottle of the old man's beer. He hadn't laid plans for what he was going to do. He hung around the house trying to formulate a strategy that would be workable and believable to the police. It would have taken the imagination of James Herbert to write a way out of this one. So he called his mum. He told her he had just killed grandma and grandpa and wanted to come

home. Naturally, it wasn't something that his mother fancied happening so she told him to phone the police and they would be able to help him out. He did just that. When the police arrived he was sitting on the front stoop with the rifle across his knees. Naturally, the police were a little nervous, they didn't fancy having to tackle the giant teenager. They were considerably relieved when he laid down his rifle and submitted meekly to being manacled.

The psychiatrist called in to examine him found an extremely mentally disturbed teenager. Completely amoral with an instinct for settling disputes the easiest way he knew how – by brute force. The report went on to say that Kemper felt very antagonistic towards his mother, he considered that she had abandoned him when he needed her and left him to the mercy of his grandparents who he now saw as ogres. It was strongly recommended that if Kemper were ever released into society again, it should not be into the care of his mother. Five years later the examining board of the institution declared that Edmund Kemper was fit to be released into the care of the community. Not only that but he should be paroled into the care of his mother. His mother was assured that Edmund was now a model citizen, wanting nothing more than to find a job and look after his family. His mother was flattered into taking him in. His sister was not so happy about it but she had recently married and was having problems of her own. Edmund again tried to turn over a new leaf. His mother got him a job as a parking attendant at the University of California where she worked as a personal assistant to the deputy head. Edmund had filled out a bit by now and had lost the gangling gait that had provoked so much sick humour at his expense. His good looks and deep friendly voice got him noticed. He even became a bit of a sport for some of the rowdier girls on the campus. He had a car now and used to pick a girl up in one of the cafés and take her for a ride in the country. He would always make

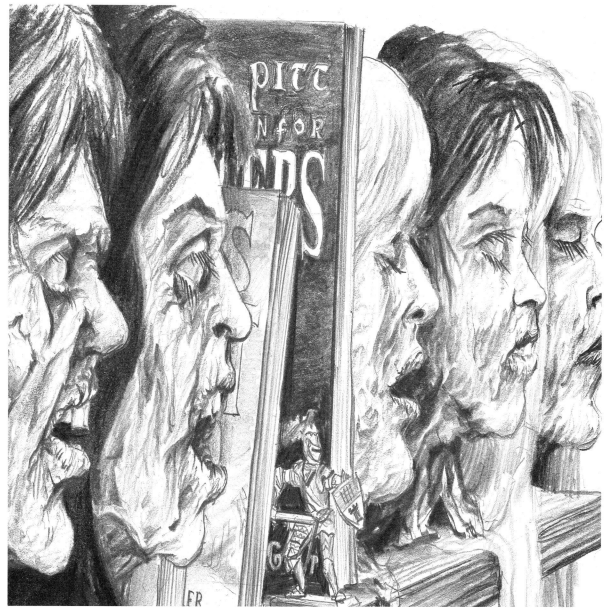

Edmund Kemper kept the heads of the women he murdered on his sideboard as trophies and sex objects.

a play for her but it was nothing a healthy co-ed couldn't handle. He was under a strain. It was just a refinement of what he used to get when he was younger. He had again become a figure of fun, a 'dare-date'. He began to figure out ways that he could stop the girls getting away. It was a simple job to fix the doors of his car so that they couldn't be opened from the inside. His brooding and escalating short temper were beginning to worry his mother. She tried to be sympathetic and controlled but everything she said came over as nagging. Kemper moved out and took a flat in San Francisco. San Francisco was a wide open city at this time and Kemper was decidedly less remarkable than a lot of the other new-agers that had taken up residence there. Familiar with life on the campuses now, Kemper targeted Fresno State College. He hung around on the road leading from the campus to the interstate highway. It was well frequented by college kids looking for a free ride home. Anita Luchese and Mary Anne Pesce decided to go home for Anita's brother's birthday party. They could have afforded to go by train or bus but decided to hitch-hike. It was all about freedom and doing your own thing, man. It was not a wise move with Kemper lurking in a lay-by. He watched them walk past, waited a few minutes then drove up to them and offered a lift. He looked pleasant enough and they assumed he was a student or possibly a teacher. He took them towards the State Highway but turned off before reaching it claiming that he knew a short-cut. By the time the two girls began to have doubts about their helpful patron, they were off the road and into a clump of trees near a picnic area. As soon as the car slid to a halt Kemper whipped out a knife. He demanded that the girls strip off. They refused so he slashed at Anita with his knife. Horrified, the girls tried to leap out of the car. They found that Kemper's carefully engineered door locks would not open. Kemper, in a rage, got out. Mary Anne had the wit to lock the door on her side

and then reach across and lock the driver's door. Kemper's rage when he found himself locked out of the car was fearsome. He attacked the car, threatening to turn it over. Anita had now fainted through loss of blood. Mary Anne was terrified. Her wits deserted her and when Kemper screamed at her to open the door she was so frightened that she obeyed. Still in a towering rage Kemper, dragged the girls from the car and stabbed them repeatedly. When he recovered, he realised he was in an exposed position. At any moment he might be discovered by a strolling pedestrian from the picnic site. He hastily bundled the girls in the boot of his car and drove off towards the mountains. In his mind he had already rehearsed his next move. He pulled into a secluded spot part way up the mountain and took the two bloody bodies to a ravine he had already selected on a reconnoitre into the hills. Before he disposed of the bodies, he cut off their heads and placed them in plastic bags. He pushed the bodies into the ravine and drove back to his room excited about the grisly trophies he had on the back seat.

Kemper now thought he had ironed out any faults in his system. For one thing he wasn't going to find himself locked out of the car again. Next up was Aiko Koo, a dance student in a hurry. She jumped into Kemper's car with what can only be described as alacrity when he offered her a lift. It was her only chance to get to her dance class on time. She soon had reason to regret her impetuosity. When she realised that she was not being driven to her dance school, she also tried to leap out of the car. The special locking device defeated her. She was a small girl but strong and fought fiercely. She died from multiple stab wounds. Once again, he disposed of the body at the foot of the mountains. The head he kept as a trophy. Back in his room he placed the severed head beside the other two and laid on his bed and gloated over them. He became sexually aroused and was driven to gratify his sexual urges on the heads. If Kemper had always been strange, he had now become horrifyingly practical. Well, as practical as a raving monster can be. The papers and TV were full of reports of the missing girls. It made Kemper feel good to be the centre of so much attention. The next girl he picked up at a service station. He waited until she left and followed. He saw her being turned down by a truck driver and pulled up along side her. He introduced himself and offered her a lift part of the way to San Francisco. Marie Costen was grateful. She was from the University and had been to visit her boyfriend. They had a row and she walked out. She was so busy reminiscing over the past few days that it was only when Kemper stopped by the side of a deserted road and pulled out his knife that she got worried. Her worries didn't last long. Kemper drove his well-honed blade straight into her throat. She died without a sound. Kemper wasn't on his usual beat with a well-planned disposal place carefully picked out. He had become so confident that he just rolled the body into a ditch and, with a couple of slashes of his sharp knife, separated her head from her body. He could hardly wait to get home to his row of heads and the sexual release they offered. He had another reason to be excited: he had slipped a succulent piece of Marie's torso into his plastic bag and looked forward to having it for his supper.

The thrill of being a feared killer was heightened by contact with the men paid to look for him. He found the bar where the off-duty policemen drank after work and sat around listening to their talk. It was mostly about Kemper whom they had dubbed the 'Co-ed Killer'. He even became friendly with one or two of them. He learned from them that the long-running crime series *Police Story* was a great place to learn about police methods and what they were doing. While he was flaunting himself before the police, he was still on the murder trail. He wasn't a great innovator and the methods used in his first murders stood him in good stead for those he committed

subsequently. But mentally he was coming apart. He now had six heads on his shelf and he was abusing himself so much that he was beginning to show the effects of his macabre debauchery on his face and in his manner. He went back to brooding over how his mother had deserted him, shipped him out of her life and into the loveless regime of his grandparent's home. It was getting harder to find girls willing to accept a ride from a stranger. Police notices were everywhere warning that the 'Co-ed Killer' could strike anywhere. The newspapers were full of stories about defenceless girls being the killer's natural prey and descriptions of the mutilations and decapitations were given out as warnings to the unwary. After a frustrating evening without even sighting a hitch-hiker, Kemper drove back to his mother's house in Santa Cruz. By the time he got there he had worked himself up into a homicidal state. His mother was in bed when he let himself into the house. He sat in the dark and felt the anger and frustration build. He laid all his problems on his mother. If she had been different. If she had loved him more. If she hadn't sent him away. The rage built in him. It was time to teach his mother that she should have looked after him better. He went into the kitchen and quietly opened the little cupboard door under the sink. The box of tools was still where he had left it. He took out a heavy hammer and stood and considered his next move. He didn't consider it for long – his mind had already been made up on the drive from San Francisco. His mother didn't move as he crept silently into the room and stood over her. He raised the hammer and smashed it with all the weight of his huge body behind it, into her skull. The first blow was a release and he smashed away at the body of his mother until he was exhausted. He sat by the side of the bed and looked at the bloody body. He felt the sexual urge rise as it always did after a killing. Slowly, he stood up and took the big hunting knife out of his pocket. Grasping the wet, sticky hair he sliced into her neck and severed her head. He held the ghastly trophy in front of him. His rage hadn't abated. The mouth was hanging open. Crudely, he hacked out the tongue that had never said the things that he wanted to hear. He found a bag and put the head in it. He contemplated returning to San Francisco but the thought of the long drive after all his exertions didn't appeal. He fixed himself a sandwich and went to his room.

The sound of the telephone ringing woke him. It was Sarah Hallett, his mother's best friend. She was surprised to find him there but he explained that he had found himself free for a few days and thought he'd drop in to see his mother. Sarah asked to speak to his mother. The situation was going pear-shaped. He should have returned to San Francisco and established an alibi. Now he had Sarah able to testify that he had been in the house, if not at the time of the actual murder, at least early the following morning. She had to be silenced. His mother was in the bath, he explained, but she would like Sarah to come round for dinner, a sort of celebration of his return. Surprised, she none the less agreed. Kemper spent the day cleaning up the house and thinking about what he was going to do when Sarah arrived. She was right on time. Kemper didn't hang around. She walked past him. He closed the door, stepped up behind her and his huge hands closed around her neck. He kept up the pressure until she stopped breathing then let her drop to the floor. He took out his knife and went down on his knees beside her. It took him only a few seconds to cut off her head. It was so much of the ritual of murder that nothing would stop him claiming his trophy. He then had intercourse with the body, put the head in a plastic bag and went out to his car. He had left it out of sight behind the house. He could only pray that nobody had seen it. There was nobody about. He eased out on to the road and drove slowly away. He wasn't going to risk speeding and being pulled over by an inquisitive cop and having to explain the mementoes he had in the plastic bags on the back seat.

Kemper decided not to go back to San Francisco but headed west for Pueblo. He guessed the deaths of his mother and her friend would be connected to the deaths in California because of his trade mark beheadings. He wasn't wrong. In his calmer moments the murder of his mother got to him. He holed up in a cheap motel and watched the TV. The murders were making him famous – big time. In spite of the massive manhunt and the horrific nature of the crimes, the police were getting nowhere. Kemper could stand it no longer. He put a call through to the Santa Cruz police and confessed that he was the Co-ed Killer. He wasn't the first one to make that claim. The spectacular murders had brought out every crack-head and fruit cake from coast to coast. The telephone operator had a list of questions to ask that only the real killer would be able to answer. Silence descended on the operations room when the operator signalled that her caller qualified for closer inspection. The detective who took over the call was in no doubt that the caller was their man. He kept him talking while he traced the call. He need not have bothered. Kemper was enjoying his moment. He told the policeman where he was and confirmed what he had done. The detective was afraid that his macabre caller might ring off and disappear once more. While other officers contacted the local police, Kemper unfolded his grisly tale to the shocked detective. He was still on the telephone when the State police surrounded the motel and called for him to show himself. Twenty policemen with carbines, shot guns and pistols nervously covered the door as it slowly opened and the huge figure of Edmund Kemper ambled into the sunlight.

He was taken back to California and charged with eight murders. He was fully co-operative and told his inquisitors everything they wanted to know. He faced a barrage of questions from psychiatrists and was never off the news. As the full extent of the atrocities were revealed, with details so far not publicly known, the public were fascinated by the daily revelations. His trial was a carnival with police cordons around the court house holding back the sightseers and press reporters unable to get into the packed courtroom. Through it all Kemper seemed relaxed and acted as if the tale he had to tell was the most natural detailing of events in the world. His defence made a half-hearted attempt to have him certified insane but there were no takers. The judge in his summing up seemed to be bemused by the whole affair and merely warned the jury not to be swayed by the public interest in the case but bring in a verdict based entirely on the evidence. He was more interested in avoiding making a statement that could possibly be the basis for a re-trial than airing his own opinions. The jury hardly needed to leave the court room to agree on the verdict: guilty of murder in the first degree on all eight charges. When the clerk of the Court read out the verdict, Kemper nodded. Asked if he wished to say anything, he smiled at the judge and asked him to pass a death sentence on him. The judge took no notice of the plea and committed him to life imprisonment.

12
Ivan the Terrible

Ivan IV, the Tsar of Russia, was not the sort of man of whom you would wish to get on the wrong side. In fact, for a lot of people he came into contact with, it would have been much healthier for them if they had never left the dacha. He was an ardent admirer of Vlad Tepes and, in homage to his idol, repeated the comedy of nailing a courtier's hat to his head when he was a bit tardy in whipping it off in his presence. Ivan was born in 1530 and grew into a six footer with wide shoulders and a nose that was destined to make many a maiden's eyes water. He was paranoid about the amount of power his Boyars held and they bore the brunt of most of his imaginative cruelty. Most, but not all. Ivan occasionally liked to pick up a peasant who caught his eye and have fun with him. Few survived the despotic ruler's idea of an amusing day out.

He was a man given to excess in many ways. Take what happened when he decided to wed. He didn't cast a lecherous eye over the ladies of the court or send messages out to a select number of foreign courts who had a wench or two of suitable birth, age and beauty and wait for a bride bearing a standard trade agreement. He sent out a cattle-call for virgins and 1500 turned up at the gate. Few of them returned home in the same state as they had arrived. After a process of elimination he arrived at Anastasia Zakharina-Koshkina. She lasted the longest of his seven brides and bore him six children and single-wombedly started the Romanov dynasty, destined to hold power until the peasants got above themselves in 1917 and threw them out.

The overthrow of the Romanovs in the 20th Century was because they had become weak and ineffectual as a ruling elite. Something that could not have happened to Ivan. He made sure that everyone knew precisely who was boss and what would happen if they forgot it for a moment. He also had a charming way of rewarding his fans when they did well. He decided that he wanted the most beautiful cathedral to stand in Moscow. He studied hundreds of plans submitted for the contract and was pleased to award the job to a couple who sounded like a music-hall turn, Postnik and Barma. They managed to produce just what he wanted. He spent many hours wandering around the building site followed closely by the fêted and fated, architects. Not a brick or an embellishment went into the work that didn't have his blessing. When it was finally complete, he stood for hours on an elevated platform marvelling at the beautiful work of art delivered to him by the faithful Postnik and Barma. In the evening he had a great feast and they were his honoured guests and he showered awards on them. If ever a couple of architects thought they had it made, it was Postnik and Barma. Their luck ran out the following morning. Ivan had them picked up and brought to him. He reiterated how pleased he was with the way they had turned his dreams into reality in the wonderful form of St Basil's cathedral. He swore they deserved all the honours heaped on them... *but,* and

Ivan the Terrible displayed his horsemanship by cutting off the heads of those who had offended him at full gallop.

it was a big *but*. What if, with the experience they had gained working for him, they went off and built an even more magnificent building. Postnik and Barma were beginning to feel a little disturbed as they had noticed the 'buts' creeping in. As well they might. They profusely assured Ivan that they would never again make an edifice that would rival the beauty and grandeur of St Basil's. Sorrowfully, Ivan shook his head and called up one of his henchman. With tears in his eyes, Ivan explained to the now fully terrified architects that he just couldn't risk the chance of his beautiful building being second class. He cried as he watched the executioner apply red-hot pokers to the eyes of the men who had produced a thing of beauty but would see it no more.

Other than the hat-nailing trick Ivan had another habit he shared with Vlad Tepes. He would disguise himself as a peddler or a friar and go out into the city and encourage the foolhardy to wax treasonous about their monarch. He carefully noted each dissident and then, before returning to his palace, would turn up for an orgy at the local brothel and get involved in a bit of gambling. He enjoyed himself moving around in disguise. He enjoyed himself even more next day when the malcontents were picked up by his stewards and brought to the palace. Ivan left the preliminaries to his men but never missed the inevitable torture that came after the talk. He didn't just watch. He is said to have invented ingenious ways to keep a man alive under torture that even the Chinese envied. The tortures he liked the most were those in which the tortured did it to themselves. Not voluntarily, of course, but inevitably. One he is said to have invented and had great joy watching was the garrotte and barrel. It was not something carried out in his favourite tavern but a rib tickler performed for his pleasure in the back courtyard of his palace. He had a huge keg set up and filled with wine or water or whatever took his fancy that day. On top of the liquid was placed a thick, close-fitting board. Above the tun was a gibbet with a thin wire noose

hanging above the floating board. Whoever happened to have displeased the Tsar was brought to the barrel in chains, hauled up and stood on the board. The chains and blindfold were removed and he found himself facing Ivan, seated on a small balcony, just above him. Ivan or one of his attendants would read out the sentence and the noose was placed over the doomed man's head. At a nod from Ivan a small bung was knocked out of the bottom of the barrel and the liquid started to leak out. For a while nothing seemed to happen. The man awaited execution either stoically or begging for mercy. When minutes went by and nothing seemed to be happening, the strain became unbearable and even the most stoic tended to look a little nervous at this point. But still the wait continued. Then the condemned man might notice that the Tsar seemed to be a little higher and the sides of the barrel a little more exposed than when he had first been levered into place. And the wire connecting him to the gallows was stretching, becoming slowly straighter. At this point the poor man began to get an idea of his fate and would try to stop the encircling noose cutting into his throat. But it was useless to struggle. It didn't matter if he got his fingers between the wire and his neck. Sooner or later the weight of his suspended body caused the wire to cut into the flesh. If the body weight was right, the wire would cut right through and tear off the unfortunate man's head. Ivan particularly liked this form of execution. He was also partial to the impaling method popularised by Vlad but he didn't want to be thought derivative, so only used it occasionally.

Ivan was fond of hunting. The problem was it often took up a lot of time and then the quarry might get away. Besides which, he always felt quite sorry for the magnificent bear or stag torn apart by the hounds. He found it much more acceptable to use a less swift but more devious prey. Especially if it was someone he detested. Prince Shuisky was such a man. Ivan ordered his huntsmen not to feed the dogs for three days. Then, on a crisp cold morning, he met Shuisky in the woods just outside Moscow and gave him the alternative of trying to outrun the hounds or being eaten alive on the spot. Shuisky at first refused to run. This upset Ivan terribly, so he had him whipped and brought up the dogs. Shuisky now realised that Ivan was serious, and so accepted the 10-minute start that he was allowed and ran off through the trees. Ivan gave him the full 10 minutes and then let the dogs go. He rode after them at breakneck speed to ensure that he was in at the kill. He was extremely fond of using the elements for his entertainment. When a priest forgot to mention Ivan's mother, Helena Glinska, in his prayers for the royal family he had him stripped naked and hauled to the top of his church roof. A rope was tied around his neck and he was allowed to slide down the snow-covered roof and over the side. Ivan ordered that the poor man's hands were left free so that he could scrabble for his live. It didn't help. When he survived he was just hauled up again and shoved off on his skin toboggan. He didn't survive the second push.

One of Ivan's pet ambitions was to marry into the English royal family and get himself a bit of land outside the Steppes. He was quite keen on Elizabeth but she was determined to remain the 'Virgin Queen' and, anyway, couldn't stand the cold. He had a shot at hooking up with some of the nobility, and was even on a half promise at one time, but his reputation had gone before him and the whole idea was shelved indefinitely. Like his contemporary, Henry VIII, he was a little careless with his wives. His first wife died, after delivering the nucleus of the new dynasty, in bed of an unspecified illness. His second wife died after falling down some inconveniently placed steps in the palace. The third one was a bit of a mistake and only lasted two weeks after contracting a fatal illness – presumably on her wedding night. This made room for number four who managed to survive for three years before wisely renouncing her marriage vows and nipping off to a nunnery. He went through another three wives and boasted of 50-plus concubines he kept on tap as well as a couple of high-class hookers who Ivan kept about the palace. Most of the wives who died did so in suspicious circumstances but nobody was foolhardy enough to suggest any such thing. As he got older, Ivan became more cruel in his dealings. Anyone could find themselves the butt of his murderous sense of humour. A messenger brought him a note from one of his Boyars. After delivering the message the bearer turned to go before Ivan had given him permission. Ivan had the man's feet nailed to the floor to remind him not to leave before he was given permission in the future. His temper became so uncontrollable that in a fit of rage he struck his son and heir, Ivan Jr, with an iron bar, killing him on the spot. Although described as 'a devout Russian Orthodox', many of his acts of cruelty were directed against members of the church. He had the Metropolitan of Moscovy strangled for no other reason than that he disagreed with the Tsar's lifestyle. The Metropolitan of Novgorod also upset him. Ivan ordered him to be stripped and then dressed in a jester's outfit. Just to humiliate him further, he insisted that he carried an inflated pig bladder and a horn and skipped through the freezing streets of Great Novgorod blowing the horn and hitting people with the pig skin. When the priest was near exhaustion, Ivan brought up a brood mare and insisted that the Metropolitan was married to the animal. Nobody dared argue with him. Once the marriage was well and truly solemnised, Ivan insisted that it was consummated. Then the priest was stripped of his jester's robes and driven out of the city nude. Ivan issued an edict saying that anyone helping the poor man would be subjected to a similar fate. It was an unnecessary pronouncement. Ivan stayed in the city for five weeks. Every day he had his chair brought out into the square. A batch of townspeople, men, women and children, were then selected at random and brought before him. At his signal, soldiers descended on the huddled, terrified citizens and slaughtered them where they stood. Ivan would then walk among the bodies and finish off any that still displayed a vestige of life. At the same time, he sent men to destroy the city. Every decent building within a 100-mile radius was systematically razed to the ground and the livestock stolen or slaughtered.

In Mongolia there is a game played on horseback that is a bit like mounted rugby. When the mood is on them, the villagers turn out to watch as the horsemen charge up and down wrestling over a calf-skin packed with straw. Ivan was very fond of this game but insisted on including his own variation. He suspected some of his counsellors of plotting against him. This was an on-going phobia that dictated a large number of the Tsar's actions. He had them rounded up and taken to a field where the game was about to take place. He instructed holes to be dug in the ground and his erstwhile counsellors were buried up to their neck in them. With 100 men, all intent on pleasing the boss, charging up and down the field, they didn't last long. Any that did survive Ivan finished off himself by riding at them, Cossack-style, and slicing off their heads with his sword. Ivan added many countries to his empire. It wasn't easy and when things went wrong, he would order terrible punishments. Cutting off hands, feet, noses and ears was fairly commonplace. An old Turkish custom of sewing a malcontent into the belly of a horse and leaving him to die was done less often as it meant slaying a valuable horse if there wasn't a dead one handy. A more sporting use of horses could be arranged by tying the doomed man to a couple and driving them in different directions. The Tsar would make bets on how long it was until legs or arms were torn off. But Ivan didn't have it all his own way. The authority of the Turks, who had held sway in that part of the world for years, was on the wane and there were many would-be monarchs fighting over the land. Ivan's main opponent was the cousin of Erzebet Bathory, Stephen, King of Poland.

Ivan didn't last long after his 54th birthday. He wasn't a well man. He had become thin and stooped and walked with some difficulty. His huge head lolled forward as if the muscles in his neck were not strong enough to support it. He died famously playing chess with one of his favourites and the man who would ultimately succeed his surviving son Fedor, Boris Godunov. To atone for his sins, Ivan asked Godunov to shave a tonsure on his head and dress him in a friar's habit. He wanted to die as the monk, Jonah.

13
Comte Gilles de Rais

When it comes to murderers, le Comte Gilles de Rais is in the premier league, at least looking at him through the lens of the new-born 21st Century. In his day he was looked on as nothing more than a bit of a rogue. A bonne companion for the lusty son but someone to be avoided if you had been blessed with daughters. Gilles was the ultimate man's man. He fought shoulder to shoulder with the daring but dateless Jeanne d'Arc, the pious maiden from Domremy, had the ear of the Dauphin, was blessed by the clergy and was filthy rich. By the time he was 24 years old he was truly in a position to say 'been there, done that' and got the chain-mail equivalent of the T-shirt. What does a wealthy young man-about-court do to top that sort of life? Well, there were the arts. He spent millions collecting works of art and endowing churches and museums. He was so wealthy that even his friend the Dauphin began to be jealous. However, Gilles was astute enough to not want an eyeball to eyeball with his liege lord. There was a pretty good chance that de Rais, circa 1428, was in a position to do the crown a lot of mischief if he were so inclined. But if he won and had to take over the running of the country, it would cut down on his leisure time, just when he was beginning to enjoy the comforts of hearth and home. So he increased his donations to good causes, which meant mainly keeping the clergy in the luxury they were used to, and kept well shot of any chance of being branded among the several factions tainted by intrigue.

The Vampire lobby have tried to claim Gilles de Rais as the founding member of the modern fang club. He predates those other false claimants Vlad Tepes and Erzebet Bathory by over 100 years. He, like them, also failed his medical as a real, in your jugular, halitosis-ridden, undead, blood sucker. He was very much alive, disdained the niceties of the jugular, had no more halitosis than any 24-year-old boyo who had never cleaned his teeth and lived on a diet of meat – roasted or raw. His revels began fairly abstemiously, just a few fatted calves, a flock of sheep and half a cellar of wine. And, of course, plenty of the hard stuff that the monasteries started distilling and churning out about this time. The entertainment was equally restrained. With major ecclesiastics attending the revels, it had to be. A few dozen wenches from the surrounding countryside doing their bit for church and country, and an interesting variety of boys. Gilles had been a soldier since he could strap on grieves and urinate from horseback. A Spartan life, with only the company of like-minded youths to provide relief for his pubescent sexual urges, had done little for the poetic side of the young Comte's nature. There was the odd bit of rape but in spite of rank, he usually found that the bigger and lustier members of the hoi poloi got there first and spoiled the fruit for the more selective and cultured. The turnover in boys was greater than the turnover in girls, in spite of the fall out from pregnancy and their generally slighter body mass. It was acknowledged that boys were more fun. They squealed louder, lasted longer and were prettier than the girls. After all, the general opinion of the time was that you had a girl for fun, a woman for breeding and a boy for love. Once Gilles had perfected the logistics, he began to broaden the entertainment base. Before long, it was difficult to tell when a rave finished and the next orgy started. His parties were the talk of cultured France and not to be on the A-list was considered a social stigma that few could survive. At this point in history, before deviants like bluff King Hal of England and the German heretic Martin Luther had hacked at the foundations of the Roman Catholic church, the clergy were all powerful. They could hand out preferments or destroy careers without spilling Holy Water. But entertaining the ecclesiastics was an expensive business and before long even Gilles de Rais' vast fortune became more a matter of reputation and artistic accounting than gold in the treasure chest. There were plenty of experts on hand to advise him, most of them recommended by members of the cloth. Gilles considered that he had done more than his share in securing a place in the hereafter and turned to the slightly dodgy practice of alchemy. The 15th Century was *the* era of the alchemist. Every self-promoting chemist who could distil a poisonous draught from a bunch of Deadly Nightshade berries or a love potion from dried bull's semen, claimed to be able to do a profitable line in turning base metal into gold. Gilles had plenty of base metal, gold was a little harder to come by. By the time he realised that the gold he was getting from the alchemist's stone was costing him more than it was worth on the open market, his financial affairs had moved from dodgy to disastrous. As his fortune plunged, his parties became wilder and even more corrupt. He did try to make a fiscal comeback by charging a fee to his invitees but the churchmen, to an obi, refused to put their hand in the offertory box. Without their support, Gilles realised he would be finished. The Dauphin, elevated to the status of Charles VII by the sustained efforts of Gilles and the slayer of the English, Joan, had reading difficulties when Gilles appealed to him for help. Especially as John of Nevers, a cousin of Gilles and jealous of Gilles friendship with the monarch, had sequestered the de Rais lands in the north-west of France after an argument over wills. A word from a determined Dauphin could have helped de Rais out. But the king had just discovered Bruges lace and hadn't time to help out an old friend.

Gilles de Rais did what any self-respecting Comte would do under the circumstances. He threw bigger and wilder parties. If he was going to go, he was going in style. Up until now, the deaths that had occurred at his revels had been unfortunate. Naked boys running the gauntlet of intoxicated men flailing at them with small whips with pieces of metal embedded in them had plucked out the odd eye or two and sometimes the wounds had turned septic and the boys had died. But it was all good fun and the men responsible were sorry that they had deprived other guests of having fun with the boys. Contests to see who could run the farthest with a hot coal strapped to their head produced a few fatalities but not so many they interfered with the entertainment. Donkeys mounting maidens was considered good clean fun, something to ignore during dinner.

Now the mood of the extravaganzas turned nasty. de Rais' parties, instead of being amusement for lads of a similar ilk, became satanic riots. Before, Gilles de Rais was guilty of nothing more than was acceptable at that time. When the lives of peasants were held in no more value than that of a pig or a ram and the lord of the manor had uncontested *droits du seigneur* over anyone living on his land or in his service. Life was cheap. de Rais now began actively to pursue the cruel and the sadistic. Skinning alive was popular. Gilles himself boasted that so skilled was he with the skinner's knife that he could skin a boy without spilling more than a cupful of blood. Like most murderers who anticipate the deed and plan for it as if it is an entertainment, de Rais was fascinated by blood. He liked the feel of it, the texture. He was aroused by the way it bubbled brightly from a severed artery. At one party, he had a number of boys suspended over the dining table on hooks driven through their chests. He then cut off the penis and he and his fellow revellers drank the gushing blood. He had a particular fascination with women's stomachs. He

Marshall of France, Comte Gilles de Rais, was a prolific party giver.

would stretch a selected girl out on a table and slit open her belly from vagina to navel and examine her innards. If he found a foetus, he would sit it in a chalice and give it a place at the table as a macabre uninvited guest. Often he would slice off the breasts or part of the buttocks and either eat them raw or command his chef to cook them. For sport he would tie a boy to a board and make wagers with his guests. Odds were given for a designated part of the body, finger, arm, leg et cetera. With either a short throwing spear or bow, the contestant would say what he was going to hit and make a bet. If he missed or hit the wrong target, de Rais cleaned up. If the player killed the target, he was made to pay a hefty forfeit. Dwarves and boys, dressed in gladiator costume, fighting to the death were also considered good entertainment. Excess mounted on excess. The Churchmen began to give the Nobleman's gatherings a miss and with them went many of their retinue. By now, de Rais didn't care. He vented his pent-up fury on the helpless bodies of the boys and girls brought to him by his procurers. It took men of very strong stomach to go to one of his dinners now. Before they had even got to the petit fours, he would have children brought to the table and slaughtered where they stood. Then, he would sit in the blood and viscera and eat choice pieces from the dismembered body. While he was rich and powerful, he could do this and get away with it. With his profitable land in the north west now in the hands of his cousin John, by decree of the King, the church was no longer interested in sustaining his popularity now that he was broke and vulnerable. Then, he committed an unforgivable sin in the eyes of the church. A mendicant friar turned up at the gates. As it was impossible to turn a Holy Man away without at least watering and feeding him, he was invited in. When he saw de Rais being beastly to a servant, he criticised him. The monk was lucky to escape with his life. At this stage de Rais was no longer able, nor wanted, to control his rages. He beat the monk up and then horse-whipped him out of town. The ecclesiastical authorities, the same men who had been privileged to be invited to the Comte's parties and share the excitement of his bloody games, decided that laying a whip on a Holy Man, however lowly, put him outside the pale. He was accused of every ungodly act the Priests could think of, and in 1440, he was put on trial. It was an interesting case in that, like the Priests at the time of Jesus, the ecclesiastical courts could not issue a death penalty. So the job had to be done through the secular courts. It made no difference to the verdict. The torture that de Rais was subjected to, and which wrung every confession out of him that his fevered brain could invent or his inquisitors could suggest, was just to show that no foot would remain unbroken or skin unseared by the torturers brand in the search for truth. But the verdict had been handed down long before. When Cousin John of Nevers had persuaded the church and the monarch that he was the rightful owner of the de Rais lands. As Jeanne d'Arc had discovered nine years earlier as she waited for Marshal of France le Comte Gilles de Rais to rescue her from the flames, nobody likes a loser. de Rais was executed and Charles VII didn't raise a hand to stop the death of the man who had put him on the disputed throne of France.

14
John Williams

Seventy-seven years before Jack the Ripper laid down his challenge to be the most celebrated serial killer in history, another series of murders were committed in roughly the same area which had the citizens of the East End of London in fear of their lives. It was in an area known as 'The Stews'. London had grown on the wind. The prevailing wind from the west. The centre of London was inhabited by an industrial elite who made most of it a cesspool of opposing stenches: soap manufacturers, skinners and dyers, rubber curers, butchers and every other trade that seemed to be as smelly as it was essential. And the streets! The gutter for carrying away the effluent ran along the middle of the narrow streets and collected in pools in the lower levels. The River Fleet was still above ground at this time and was a stinking, open sewer filled with decaying carcasses and the contents of rudimentary toilets emptying straight into the river. These little London brooks that had once been the reason for moneyed people to move into the area before the tradesmen decided to pollute the water, ran straight into the tidal waters of the River Thames. Twice a day the ebb and flow of the river stirred the stinking mess and turned the air foul. Especially in the east. So the property to the west of the city became prized as dwellings for the rich, and the poor and destitute had to make do with the unsavoury environment in the east. This meant that the flood of immigrants into the city in the early 19th Century finished up in the area around Aldgate Pump. Mr Timothy Marr's shop at 29 Ratcliffe Highway, (now just The Highway) was well placed to take advantage of the goods delivered in the nearby docks. Not only did he sell fine lace, silk and other materials over the counter but he also did a good trade as a wholesaler. Some of the deals he did off the docks might be a little 'peppered' as the euphemism was then, (read 'fell off the back of a lorry'), but he was generally considered an upright citizen. He had a pretty wife, Celia, adorable baby, Timothy Jr, a trusted servant girl, called Mary and a young apprentice, James Biggs. He had more than recovered his initial investment in the business and was looking forward to moving out of the noisome docks area and maybe taking a little place in the country at Paddington or maybe Kensington. But he had the misfortune to meet John Williams. Williams was a hard man. He liked to think of himself as an entrepreneur. His entrepreneurial skills usually involved getting an interest in a worthwhile business and reaping a satisfying reward without risking his own capital. He was slightly older than Marr and a stylish dresser but he wasn't much to look at. Shortish, strangely auburn–blonde hair and a pinched, sickly face. He combated his physical short-comings by wearing only the most expensive clothes he could acquire. Marr was happy to supply him with the occasional frippery or length of cloth in exchange for introductions to some of the interesting people Williams knew. The atmosphere between the two changed when Marr refused to take Williams on as a partner. Williams, of course, wanted his share for nothing. In exchange, he promised Marr protection from the gangs that made the streets so unsafe. Marr considered this an insult to his manhood. He was an ex-seaman and had lived in the area all his life and knew how to survive. Williams didn't like

opposition. He warned Marr what would happen to his wife and child if one of the gangs became so violent that he was unable to control it. Marr still resisted. He then made the foolish mistake of talking to some of the other tradesmen that where getting the benefit of interest from John Williams. It was decided that the time had come to fight back. It wasn't long before Williams got to hear about Marr's efforts to found a vigilante group. He wasn't really worried. Just affronted. He paid good money to the Bow Street Runners for information and protection and Marr was trying to side step this. He had to be taught a lesson. And John Williams took delight in being the teacher.

The Marr family was working late finishing stock-taking. It was too late to start cooking a meal so Mary the maid was sent out to buy some oysters. As she left she saw Williams, who was well known to her, walk along the opposite side of the street, deep in conversation with some men. He didn't see her and she hurried on. The men with Williams left him opposite the Marr shop. He waited a few moments and then crossed the road. Marr was just shutting up shop. When Williams tried to push in, Marr barred his way. Williams explained to him that he had accepted that their differences were irreconcilable but insisted that he had a deal to put to him that would make them both rich men. Marr made the fatal error of stopping to listen. He let Williams in, pulled down the shutter and turned over the closed sign. As he turned, Williams drove the spike of a heavy maul hammer deep into his neck. As a reflex action Marr threw his arms around his assailant but even as he did so he died. Blood spurted from the severed carotid artery and splashed on to Williams fine clothes. He savagely pushed the still standing body of Marr aside and frantically tried to sponge off the blood. All that happened was the stain grew bigger. He aimed a couple of kicks at the dead body at his feet and calmed himself down. He had only intended to kill Marr as an example to others, not to cross him. Ruining his suit put the whole affair on to another plane. He moved towards the

back of the shop. He saw someone coming towards him and stepped into the shadows. James, the apprentice, called to Mr Marr and when he didn't answer went into the shop. Williams didn't wait. He swung his bloody hammer but in the near darkness miscalculated. The hammer glanced off the wall and struck James in the arm. He screamed with pain and tried to run away. Williams was too quick for him. As the blows rained down on him the sound of a baby's cry could be heard in the distance. Timothy Jr had been left in the warmth of the kitchen where he was out of the way. As Williams hacked in a silent frenzy at the body of the young apprentice, Celia came to the top of the stairs to see what was going on. In the dark she could make out nothing. No one answered her call so she went to the downstairs kitchen. The baby by this time had got itself into a real state. As Celia bent over it, Williams grabbed her and threw her to the floor. When she tried to get up he kicked her in the stomach and at the same time smashed down on the baby's crib. It was an old-style crib with a little hood over the baby's head. One blow with the hammer destroyed what little protection the hood might have afforded. Ignoring pain, Celia scrabbled at the murderer's legs. He kicked her off. She fell heavily against the wall. She watched in a daze, unable to move, as Williams picked up the baby, held it up so that she could see what was happening – and smashed the baby's skull with his hammer. He laughed and threw the tiny body down beside the mother. Celia just stared at it. Although her mind was clear, she was unable to get a response from her body. Williams pulled a carpenter's chisel from his inner pocket. He flourished it in front of Celia's face just to make sure she understood what was going on, then he deliberately ran it across the baby's neck, practically severing the head. He picked the baby up by the feet and let the blood drain away over Celia's head. With a twist of his strong wrist he threw the body back in the crib and turned his attention to the mother. She had recovered somewhat by now. He hunched down in front of her and as she opened her mouth to scream,

John Williams killed Timothy Marr and his family using a maul hammer and chisel.

he drove the razor sharp chisel that he had just used on her child straight into her windpipe. She slumped backwards, scrabbling at the ruins of her neck. Williams showed no mercy. He steadied himself and then drove the spike of his hammer straight into her head. After the horrors she had witnessed, it was probably a blessed release.

It was about this time Mary the maid came back into the picture. She had been unable to get oysters locally and had been to Wapping Hard in the hope that she might be able to get some straight off a boat. No luck. The house was in darkness when she returned. It didn't immediately strike Mary as strange. The living quarters were at the back of the house. She tapped on the door and waited. No reply. She knocked louder. Williams was at the kitchen sink trying to repair the damage the blood had done to his clothes. The knock came again. He went to the door that led out to the area in front of the kitchen and, keeping well back, looked up the stairs. Mary knocked on the door again. He considered what to do. He knew who she was and that she wasn't likely to come to a decision to leave without getting a reply. He picked up his trusty hammer and went up the inside stairs as stealthily as the creaking boards would allow. Beside the shop was an entrance that led directly into the living quarters. Mary was now becoming seriously concerned. She thought of going down and banging on the kitchen window. A slight noise behind the door attracted her attention. She was about to call out when she suddenly had the feeling that all was not well. At that moment the next-door neighbour, a pawnbroker, came out of his shop. Mary quickly ran to him and told him that she was sure something was wrong in the house. She volunteered the information that she believed whatever was amiss was still going on and that there was a stranger in the house. The pawnbroker, a man well aware of the dangers of living in that neighbourhood, told Mary to get the Watchman and went through his shop to the yard at the rear. It was protected by a 10-foot wall. He put a ladder against the wall and shinned up it. It was pitch black on the other side and he had to move cautiously. He berated himself for not bringing a lantern. As he neared the rear of the house, he could see a faint light coming from one of the windows. The back door was open. He crept cautiously in. He almost stumbled over the body of James. The floor was slippery with blood. The pawnbroker edged past the body and opened the front door. A couple of Runners had already arrived and pushed past Mary and went into the house. Mary followed. One of the Runners tried to hold her back to guard her from the horrors but she wanted to see if the baby was unharmed. When she saw the cot and the mutilated body of the baby and her mistress, she fainted.

Mary was questioned closely by the Bow Street Runners. They were a bit suspicious about her fortuitous excursion to find oysters. When they widened their questioning to admit the possibility that others may have been involved, Mary remembered seeing John Williams on the opposite side of the road as she left on her errand. Williams was picked up and questioned. He admitted being in the area at the time when Mary said she saw him, even said he remembered seeing Mary walking along the road, but he claimed that he was on the way to see a bare-knuckle prize fight in Whitechapel and produced witnesses to prove that he was there all evening. It looked as if it was going to go down as just another unsolved crime.

John Williams had now got the taste for blood. He had a history of violence but it usually stopped at a disciplinary beating or a cudgel across the knees. Now he wanted to see the blood flow. Abraham Mellor had been a vociferous member of the group of interested citizens that Marr had been trying to motivate when he was killed. He was a lighterman as had been his father and grandfather before him. He had been brought up to take into account the graft on the waterfront and he had nothing against paying his dues and oiling the way to anything extra that was going. Williams was different. An outsider. Mellor told everyone who would listen that he wasn't going to be intimidated by a toe-rag like

Williams. The burial of the Marr family was set for the following Saturday and one of the biggest crowds ever seen in the East End turned up to give them a send-off. It wasn't that they had been particularly liked or that the majority had ever met them, it was just that the murder had been such a delicious atrocity that everyone wanted to feel a shudder of horror by just being near the victims. Abraham was one of the mourners who walked behind the coffin. Once the remains had been solemnly interred, he went off to the Bull Inn with a few of his mates and by the time he left had drunk himself silly. Bad move. John Williams was waiting for him on the way home. In normal circumstances Abraham would have torn Williams to pieces with his bare hands. In the inebriated state he was in, he couldn't even focus his eyes on the man barring his path. Williams drew out the wickedly spiked maul hammer from the special pocket in his coat. Abraham looked at him blearily and didn't try to duck as Williams sank the spike deep into his forehead. And, just because he liked it, Williams took out his chisel and sliced the dead man's neck open. He looked around to make sure nobody had seen him, wiped the hammer and the chisel on the dead man's waistcoat and calmly walked away. The body was found by the Watchman in the early hours of the morning.

The Bow Street Runners tried to suppress the news of another murder not 200 yards from the site of the Marr tragedy just a week earlier. They realised that the chances were that the same killer had done both jobs. They were getting enough flak from the public and from their superiors and they badly wanted someone under lock and key before announcing the new killing. They rounded up the usual suspects. This time, in pole position, was John Williams. They needn't have bothered. Williams had witnesses that claimed he was in their sight all evening and night at the King's Arms in Old Gravel Lane. The Runners didn't believe them but what could they do? They followed the well-known procedure of fitting-up a down-and-out and were prepared to take him to court on manufactured evidence.

They didn't have to bother. Williams was enjoying himself so much he couldn't just leave it alone and didn't let the hue and cry die down before striking again.

Williams was on a high, his feeling of invincibility led him straight into trouble. George Williamson, the publican at the King's Arms was happy to have Williams as a customer. He spent lavishly and brought in a lot of new trade. Williamson had gone along with everyone else when questioned about Williams' alibi; it was not for him to point the finger. Living in the pub with Williamson and his wife was a young girl, a cousin of Mrs Williamson called Nelly Burnett. She looked after the house and was happy to help out in the bar when the pub was busy. Williams took a shine to her and tried to get her to walk out with him. Under normal circumstances she would probably have gone out with him but a lodger had recently moved into the rooms above the pub, John Turner. They hadn't got it together yet but Nelly was smitten and John hadn't exactly repulsed her. So Nelly declined Williams' offer. It was a dangerous thing to do. Williams couldn't handle it and when Nelly went into the bar to collect the empties, he grabbed her and tried to kiss her. She resisted. The other customers looked the other way. They had no stomach for a confrontation with the local hard man. Nelly fought valiantly and would probably have had ultimately to submit to a wet kiss and a clumsy grope. Williamson wasn't having any of that. While Williams pawed feverishly at his cousin, Williamson picked up the heavy wooden 'comforter' he kept behind the bar, walked up behind Williams and whacked him behind the ear. Williams dropped to the floor unconscious. Williamson grabbed him by the collar and slung him out into the gutter. It wasn't the cleverest move he had made in his life. Williams crawled off and collapsed in the little alley beside the pub. When he woke up the pub was closed and all was quiet. He tried to clean up the fine embroidered coat he was wearing but it was beyond repair. His hammer hung heavily under his bloodied coat. He pushed himself to his feet and waited for his

surroundings to settle down. Hate built in him. He had been humiliated in front of the entire pub. By the morning it would be common gossip and the reputation he had built up, the reputation which had the local business men only too eager to seek his protection, would be in tatters. He was past rational thought. The fact that his humiliation had been witnessed by 20 or so people in the pub and the fact that he was already under investigation by the Runners meant nothing. He scaled the low wall at the back of the inn and forced a rear window into the small wash house. He had only the vaguest idea of the layout of the building but found the stairs. He took out his hammer and crept slowly upwards. The first bedroom he came to was that of George and Catherine Williamson. As he stood beside the bed Catherine woke up. Her scream was cut off by Williams' heavy hammer hitting her in the face, the spike burying itself in her eye socket. George reared up and tried to grapple with his attacker but he was full of sleep and disorientated. Williams struck hard, the first blow hit Williamson in the chest, the second in the temple. Blood poured all over Williams but he no longer cared. He took out his chisel and leaned over his victims. With an expert slash he ripped Catherine's throat apart. As he applied the chisel to her husband, the door opened and Nelly stood there, her mouth open, ready to scream. Williams leapt from the bed and swung the chisel at the startled woman, slicing through her raised fingers and biting deep into her throat. As she collapsed with hardly a gurgle, he swung his hammer and buried it deep in her collar bone. She was thrown back across the little passage and slumped against the opposite wall. Taking Williams' hammer, buried deep in the bone, with her. He rushed after her, grabbed the handle of the hammer and tried to prise it out. At that moment the lodger, John Turner, came to see what all the commotion was about. For a moment he couldn't believe his eyes. Lit only by the candle he carried he could just make out the bloody features of Nelly and the man standing over her. It was enough. He ran back up the stairs, bolted the door and ran to the window. He contemplated jumping but decided it was too high. Feverishly, he knotted a couple of bed sheets together, expecting at any moment for Nelly's assailant to force the door. He tied the knotted sheets to the bed head and shinned down them. Right into the arms of a passing Bow Street Runner. Sure that he had caught a burglar, the Runner did what all Runners were expected to do, he knocked him about to avoid any possible trouble later. Another practice quickly assimilated by the Metropolitan police when they were inaugurated a score or so years later. By this time, aroused by John's yells and the Runners commands for him to be still, neighbours had gathered. They soon told the Runners that John was who he had claimed and they reluctantly let him go. Other Runners arrived on the scene and they decided to enter the inn en masse via the drayman's door into the cellar. The scene that they discovered raised the gorge in even the hardened Bow Street Runners' throat. It was hard to imagine who could have done such a terrible thing. The Runners soon pulled themselves together. Most of them had been present at the Marr house scarcely two weeks before and they were instantly struck by the similarity of the crimes. The deep holes and the severed throats bore their own witness. And this time they had a clue. Williams had been unable to wrest the hammer from Nell's body. He had fled leaving the one thing that could link him not only to the Williamson massacre but also to the death of the lighterman, Abraham Mellor, and the Marr family. This time there were no shortage of witnesses to the animosity between killer and victim. The Runners arrested John Williams in his bed at the nearby Pear Tree Inn in Cinnamon Street. It was a fair cop. Williams had been so exhausted by the beating he had taken from Williamson and the excitement of the kill that he hadn't even bothered to get rid of his blood-stained clothes. He was held for questioning in Coldbath Fields prison and later sent to Newgate to await trial.

Williams was under no illusions about his fate. The day before he was to stand trial, he hanged himself with

one of the silk scarves that had been a present from Timothy Marr. Cheated of the spectacle of the trial and a public execution the prison authorities made the best of a bad job. They paraded Williams body through the streets on a little hand cart. They took a circuitous route so that everyone would get the chance of seeing the fiend whose suicide had condemned him without the necessity of a trial. A hole had been prepared for the body at the crossroads of Cannon Street and Cable Street. As a last tribute to the mass of people interested in the drama of the burial, the officer from the goal who had accompanied the body jumped in the grave after the body and drove a stake through its heart. An interesting little sidebar this. Burying corpses at the crossroads with a stake through the heart is a prime way of dispatching Vampires. Were they afraid that, unstaked, John Williams might raise himself from the grave and wreak further havoc on the community or was it just a sadistic little bit of grand-standing by an officer cheated of Williams hanging?

15
Alexander 'Sawney' Bean

The reason for Bean's nickname Sawney is not clear. In the dictionary it says that Sawney is a derogatory name for a Scotsman. Understandable, in the circumstances. It is, or at least was, a word used by an older generation of Cockneys. 'Sawney cow' tripped readily off the tongue in an argument. But neither use can possibly be explained by the actions of the progenitor of the most horrible and macabre family in Scotland – and most possibly the world – Sawney Bean. There are individuals who have been credited with thousands, even millions of deaths, Hitler, Stalin, Bathory and Tepes spring easily to mind, but these were in positions of influence and, to a certain degree, were allowed by their subjects to get away with their crimes. Alexander Sawney Bean was originally a one-man show. Alexander was born around 1560, an embryo farmhand with an illustrious name. He was handy with a billhook or axe and lived in a hovel that was rougher than sleeping in a midden in mid-summer. But it was life as he and his forbears knew it and there was nothing to be done but hack and hew. Then he met Doris. Doris wasn't her real name but she seems to have been able to keep that secret. Doris was little more than a child but, excited by Sawney's prowess with an axe, she dreamed of ways that they could turn his expertise to their advantage. Her parents came from a little village in Galloway, Scotland. It was near the coast and Doris used to run away from the drudgery of home life and explore the caves and hollows of the shoreline. By chance, she stumbled on a small entrance on the beach that was covered at full tide but led to a series of higher caves stretching for miles underground. She kept the knowledge to herself. A few days later she was taken into Edinburgh and sold to the same farmer that employed the Beans about 10 miles outside the city. Menial work didn't appeal. Sawney did. She fired him with thoughts of running away and living in the caves, never to be bossed about again. He liked the idea and one day he just shouldered his axe and followed Doris back to the Galloway Coast. The idyll soon turned sour. As exciting as Sawney might be swinging an axe, he had no idea how to look after himself away from home. And Doris was pregnant. Doris and Sawney were pretty near to starvation when Doris spotted a traveller on a horse coming along the coast road. She ran back to the cave and dragged Sawney and his trusty axe out of the cave and positioned him behind a gorse bush. She smartened herself up as best she could and sat by the side of the road. When the stranger came along she waved him down and told him a pathetic tale of hardship and loss. Being sympathetic he offered her a sandwich and climbed off his high horse. As soon as the stranger was relaxed with his back towards him, Sawney rushed out and decapitated him with one mighty stroke of his axe. Fearful of discovery, Doris instructed Sawney to pick up the body and take it to the cave. She followed with the head. Out of sight they quickly searched the body hoping to find food. Nothing. Doris thought of the horse and sped back to the site of the ambush hoping to find it still there. It had wandered off, probably back along the road it had come. Doris cursed. How could she be so stupid? That night they sat in silence in the empty cave, the only warmth a smoky fire. Doris went and looked at the naked body of their victim. She came to a decision.

Sawney Bean and his extended family lived off the flesh of travellers who passed their hidden cave.

If she didn't eat, she would starve to death. That she didn't intend to do. She took their victim's own knife and sliced a chunk of flesh from the thigh. Sawney watched her, not sure what she intended to do. He wasn't left in the dark for long. Doris speared the piece of meat on the point of the knife and held it close to the fire. When it was cooked, she offered it to Sawney. He declined the offering. Doris didn't care. It was all the more for her. She wolfed back the piece she had cooked and went back for more. This time Sawney couldn't resist the flagrant odour of roasting meat and accepted the piece Doris offered. They laid down to sleep with full bellies for the first time in weeks. Once the initial repugnance to eating human flesh was overcome, with little or no soul-searching, they tucked into what was left without thinking about it again. In the end there was nothing left but a pile of bones. Doris took them down to the cave mouth at full tide and slung them in. But hunger was back and Doris now knew what she must do.

The next traveller to take the coast road met the same fate as the first, and this time the horse didn't get away. The Beans feasted royally until the flesh became rancid and the air foul. Reluctantly, they threw the remains into the sea and went back to their roadside vantage point. Twice groups of men passed but they looked strong and well armed so they went on their journey unmolested. Then a young couple appeared. Doris went out to meet them and suggested that they might like to stop for some refreshments. To the tired and thirsty couple it seemed like a sporting offer so they followed Doris. As soon as they left the road Sawney leapt on them and hacked them to pieces. Back in their retreat they were delighted with their morning's work. Especially Sawney. It was the first time he had got his hands on the naked body of a dead woman. Doris watched but didn't interfere. She was expecting their first baby and was a little apprehensive about the birth. If Sawney wanted to get a thrill with a corpse, that was fine with her. She had an easy birth. She tried to get Sawney interested but his thoughts were elsewhere.

Doris recovered fast. Now that she had a child, she had to make provisions. So far it had been famine and feast. They had plenty of clothing now, and even money, but food was always going to be a problem. The idea of fishing in the sea which, literally, came through their front door, never seemed to occur to either of them. She picked over the remains of the two bodies and immersed some choice pieces in salt water. Other pieces she hung over the fire to dry out and be preserved by the fumes. Sawney watched her efforts in silence. He suggested that they take some of the money they had collected and go to the nearest village and buy some provisions. Doris patiently explained why that was not a good idea. It was a possibility that someone was looking for the people they had eaten. If it became known that they were living there, someone was bound to ask questions and come looking for them. Their safety depended on nobody ever finding out that they were there. Anybody unfortunate enough to stumble into them must be killed before they could tell what they knew. Sawney reluctantly agreed. He would have liked the chance to spend some of the money mounting up in the cave but he saw the wisdom in what Doris said and didn't raise the subject again.

The baby was scarcely six months old when Doris found herself pregnant again. It didn't bother her but it did inspire in her a need to make their surroundings more comfortable. She drove Sawney out to scour the beach for driftwood or to cut branches to make furniture. The furniture was something of which she was particularly proud. She had by now become quite a professional butcher and skinner. Sawney was all right for the rough work but the refinements were left to Doris. With the tanned skins of her victims she made cribs for the rapidly growing squad of children and seats for the rough-hewn chairs which were tied together with dried gut. Material for blankets and clothes was no problem.

Doris was perpetually pregnant. It didn't seem to worry her. She worked up a routine and expected Sawney to follow it. They were never again short of food and they never had to resort to eating horsemeat. Horses were too precious to eat. They were kept in the caves and provided milk and transport when they needed to overtake a traveller or had to drag anything back to the cave. By the time the first born was eight years old, he had two sisters and three brothers. He was also a skilled hand at skinning and butchering a corpse. He was ten when he was allowed to go on his first ambush. Sawney by this time was completely brutalised. Doris still understood what she was doing but didn't care. Still the children kept coming and it wasn't long before the eldest were coming on the raids and actually getting involved.

The increasing number of travellers leaving home and not getting to their destination didn't go unnoticed. Relatives and friends back tracking the route came to the conclusion that some of the inn-keepers were responsible for the disappearances and informed the Sheriff. He couldn't find any evidence but took a few of the less astute publicans who confessed to having put up the missing person shortly before his or her disappearance. Still the disappearances continued without leaving a clue to the cause. More inn-keepers were hanged as almost ritual sacrifices but it didn't cause the perpetrator of the crimes to desist. It did make the profession of inn-keeper decidedly dodgy and a large number packed their horse and departed for other places. Some taking the perilous coast road and ending up in pieces suspended from the ceiling of the cave. Search parties were sent out on numerous occasions. Some even looked in the cave entrance but Doris had taught her brood well. No clues to the activities inside the cave were ever discovered. Meanwhile, the Bean clan continued to grow in rude health. As the children reached puberty, they mated with their siblings and soon the children had children of their own. Sawney and Doris became the Adam and Eve of the dark side. Their children multiplied and multiplied. Soon there were 50 Beans living in the cave. The diet of human flesh was obviously healthy. But the inbreeding was not producing a race of gods. Uneducated, deprived of the stimulus of other people and ideas, the children were little more than animals. The grandchildren, put into that category purely on the age of the child and the generation of its parents, were horrendous. They cared nothing for clothes or rules. They couldn't be bothered to wait for their terrible fare to be cooked but ripped it from the still warm body and gulped it down. Sawney was completely gone, an animal like his children. Only Doris strove to keep her brood from hell and safe from discovery. She organised the ambushes so that nobody could get away to tell the tale. The clan was spread out so that anyone escaping those that actually stopped them would run into the back-up. They were so successful that even with the fast-growing Bean clan, there was always a surplus. Doris detailed her monstrous horde to take the body parts that were old or not needed and throw them into the sea. The surging tide carried them away to be deposited on distant beaches and traumatise the inhabitants of the towns. In desperation, the authorities began picking up anybody who they thought might be the killer. They hanged them out of hand and hoped the disappearances would stop. They were always disappointed. Even as the executioner swung the axe or tied the knot, the judiciary doubted their guilt. Not one of them confessed to being the phantom mugger. The disappearances had been going on for so long that they had reached legendary state. It was long before flying saucers had been invented, so the lost ones were consigned to the realm of Satan or sea monsters.

It had become such a scandal that even the King became involved. It had become obvious, from the execution of the inn-keepers, where the travellers had been last seen and where they were heading. As the inn-keepers had been proved not guilty by the continuance of the disappearances, King James opined that somewhere along this route lay the cause of the problem. No one presumed to tell him that this had been obvious for years – he was the King and on his authority the soldiers could be turned out and a systematic search undertaken. Already a number of officials had been sent out to try to find out what was happening. Few of them were ever seen again. It was almost impossible to talk anyone else into taking the murder road so the army was sent in. Three times they swept the 20-mile stretch of road. Sometimes they even ventured into the cave mouth but it didn't seem possible that anyone could live there with the sea filling the cave twice a day. Nobody was willing to probe deeper into the caves and get cut off by the tide. The Bean's luck couldn't last forever. A local landowner returning from a fair was their undoing. That and the fact that so many of the inbred children were a pleat or two short of a kilt. Doris's iron discipline, which had made it impossible for a target to escape and blow the whistle, began to slip. The rider had his wife riding pillion behind him. He was aware, as was everyone else, that the area was not the best through which to be riding alone and had come prepared with primed pistols and a drawn sword. He was also grateful to have his wife behind him to protect him from the rear. The Bean lookout sounded the view hello and the monstrous brood spread out in the usual formation. Doris sent the four interceptors in. Their proposed victim wasn't taking any chances. As the attackers moved in, he challenged them. When they didn't reply, he uncovered his pistols and fired. One of the raiders went down and a second was slightly wounded. It didn't stop the attack. The rider drew his sword and met them head on. He didn't have the alternative of fleeing. With his wife in the rear weighing down the horse he didn't have a chance of escaping. The melee drew in some of the less-disciplined Beans and they were able to drag the woman from the horse. They didn't wait to see the outcome of the ambush. The fiendish women whipped out sharp knives and began hacking pieces off her and stuffing them in their mouths while she was still alive. Others fought to get a place at the feast, they slit her throat and drank the blood. The hellish scene served to galvanise the lone rider into even greater effort. The outcome, as valiantly as he fought, was inevitable. Just when it appeared that he must succumb, a band of 30 or

so riders, also from the fair, rode up. Doris screamed at her children and they instantly retreated. leaving the mutilated corpse of the rider's wife behind.

But now that the secret of the cannibal clan was out, there was an even greater outcry. It seemed impossible that the number of people that the widowed man had claimed attacked him could have gone for so long undetected. The King was furious. He was being made to look a fool. And that was a precarious position to be in on any throne at that time – and especially on the throne of Scotland. He determined to undertake the search for the miscreants personally. He summoned the victim of the bungled ambush and listened intently to what he had to say. The man wasn't too keen on leading an expedition into his nightmare but couldn't very well tell the King to find another. There wasn't one. The King rode out at the head of 400 troops, and dozens of dog handlers with trained dogs. They started from the scene of the attack and gradually increased the area of search. The first sweep produced nothing. It wasn't good enough. The King ordered them out again. This time some of the dogs were taken along the beach. When they got to the cave entrance they began to holler. The handlers ventured a little way into the cave but the slime-covered walls and stigian darkness turned them back. They couldn't believe that anyone would choose to live in such an environment. But the dogs wouldn't let it go and continued to yelp and holler and pull the handlers back to the darkness. At last the men had to reluctantly admit that they would have to search the caves. But they were not going alone – not even with the dogs. The King ordered a squad of picked men to accompany the dogs and their handlers into the cave. They crept slowly forward, the only illumination coming from the hastily made torches they carried. Eventually they reached the inner cave where the Beans had dwelt for 25 years. The Beans were all there, blinking at the torches, unable to believe that outsiders had penetrated their stronghold. They offered no resistance and were tied up and dragged from the cave.

The soldiers searching the cave couldn't believe what they saw. Hanging from the ceiling were human body parts cured like hams. In a bubbling stock pot were more pieces of human anatomy. In a corner was a pile of coins and jewellery. Another niche held a mountain of clothes. On the walls were pictures and artefacts taken from convoys they had attacked. Everywhere there were guns and swords and personal effects. When the scene was described to the King, he couldn't believe it and made a personal inspection. What he saw haunted him for years.

The procession into Edinburgh drew a massive crowd. Few could believe that the assortment of bedraggled men and women in a bizarre array of clothes could be the ones that had held the population in fear for over two decades. The Beans had never seen anything like it. None of them had ever been away from the immediate environs of the cave. They had only ever seen people singly or in small, terrified groups. They didn't seem overawed by their new celebrity status – just interested. Now that they were in the hands of the authorities, they presented a problem. There were so many of them that they couldn't be accommodated in the prison, so they were herded into a courtyard in the castle while the King deliberated with the town authorities on how they were going to handle the matter. Not that there was any doubt about the punishment, just how and when it was to be administered. With the crowd outside baying for blood and the lack of secure accommodation for the Bean family, it was decided that a speedy end to the situation was called for. There was no point in having a trial, it would just waste time. They would be marched to Leith and executed on the spot. The two elder Beans, Alexander and Doris, were called in and they were told that they and their offspring were to be executed. Sawney said nothing. He was a great hulk of a man with a profusion of matted grey hair. Doris had run to fat but was still a powerful woman and an accomplished swearer. She was as vociferous as Sawney was silent. They were returned to the courtyard where the rest of the family was already being made ready to leave. The move to Leith was a chance for the citizens to vent their displeasure on the hellish family. A massive gauntlet that left none of the Beans unscathed. They spat and swore at their persecutors but seemed impervious to either the pain of their injuries or their fate. Once they arrived in the market square at Leith, the sentences were carried out without delay. It had been decided that, for the men, hanging or decapitation was too good for the hideous crimes they had committed. Instead they were to have their hands and feet hacked off and be allowed to bleed slowly and painfully to death. It took them a couple of hours to die. The troops made sure that Doris and the rest of the female Beans watched as their menfolk died. Then they were taken outside the castle where a great fire had been stoked up. The women, mother, daughters and granddaughters were trussed up and thrown on to the fire. They went screaming and cursing their judges.

In spite of the assurance that all the Beans had been accounted for, it was a long time before the road that passed their killing ground was used without a feeling of dread. The cave still exists but unlike many other caves along that bit of coastline, few people visit it. There has been plenty of controversy about the out-of-hand execution of the Bean family. Mama and Papa Bean were obviously up for the chop as soon as they killed their first victim. The incestuous relationships they had with their children and those they allowed their children to indulge in also made them guilty of breaking the law. There were plenty of charges to bring against the parents because they had grown up in a society in which the practices they embraced were totally illegal and immoral. But what about the children? They do not come over as little cherubs but were they guilty of the crimes for which they were executed? A crime cannot be committed unless the perpetrator is aware that he or she is committing a crime. Ignorance of the law is no defence. But does this hold good if it can be proved that those breaking a law could not possibly know that it existed? Had, in fact, been brought up to believe that the practices they saw performed on a daily basis were normal? This was the case with the offspring of the Beans. They had no way of knowing that murder wasn't the way of life pursued by everybody. No way of knowing that sex with members of your immediate family was forbidden. Food was food – and food was obtained by killing a traveller and eating him. What other way was there? With no yardstick other than their parents, no contact with the outside world, it should have been possible to argue that no crime was committed by the Bean children because there was no possible way that they could know that such a crime existed. Probably in the long run it was just as well that they were executed. If they had lived, it would have been impossible to assimilate them into society. The idiot grandchildren would have been allowed to starve and the children ostracised. Being incinerated alive might not have been the easy option but the horror of pain is in the memory. They burned and died – the finish, the end. It was then up to St Peter and his balance sheet to decide what, if anything, was their crime.

As was the custom before books and television, memorable events were enshrined in song or poem form to be spouted in the taverns and fields to keep everyone aware of recent deeds of derring-do or bloody murder. A number of odes were told of the murdering Beans.

A family inbred like serpents entwined
Had no heart and little mind
A clan of madness, a terrible scene
They cursed the earth, the family Bean
Lurking in the fog, a fearsome brood
Poor travelling folk they caught and slew'd
No graves have the victims of these ghouls and fiends
Those taken and eaten by the cannibal Beans
From their flesh they made a hideous meal
Their skins on the floor for their bairns to kneel
Their skulls a table from which to feed
Alas the victims of this Devil's breed.

They lived by the sword, were felled by the axe
And I say nothing was wrong with that
But in their hellish caves worse than any dream
Cursed with the stench of Sawney Bean

Some are haunted by the tolling bell
Some by the fiery pits of hell
But what haunts me is what we did see
When entered the larder of Sawney Bean, we.

Not exactly Tennyson but there are a couple of lines that scan. And worse:

> *Sawney Bean killed and then he ate*
> *He had a wife, a fearsome mate*
> *With bairns galore he held in terror*
> *Those travellers who pass'd in error*
> *In caves they dwell'd*
> *In caverns deep*
> *Midst shells of those they killed did sleep.*
>
> *But James of Scotland*
> *With hounds unleashed*
> *Capture'd and slew the devil's band*
> *And there was rejoicing throughout the land.*

16

Legal Murder

The search for murderers becomes a bit confusing when the art of the public executioner is taken into consideration. Does the executioner carrying out the strict code of Islam become less of a murderer because he has the comfort of the Koran when he lops of the hands of a thief or decapitates a young girl for adultery? When the inquisition was in full swing in the middle ages, was torture and burning any less horrific because it was done in the name of the Holy Cross by men of the cloth? Did crushing a baby to death with the cornerstone of a building become less of a crime because it had the approval of the head man and was expected to bring good luck to whoever lived in the house? If the men, and occasionally women, who beg to be allowed to carry out judicial executions are denied this outlet to wreak mayhem among their fellow man, do they become the killer on whom the more fortunate hangman has to practice his art?

Take James Berry for instance. He came from a comfortable background, was intelligent and well read. He could have lived out a comfortable middle-class existence in the company of his family and friends. Instead, he chose to give them all up and become the public hangman. From an early age he thought about nothing else but the thrill of taking a condemned man on his last lonely walk in the cold morning air and dropping him through a hole with a rope knotted around his neck. He hung around the prison when an execution was scheduled and sought out the company of the man who was then doing the business on the scaffold, Mr Marwood. Marwood was flattered to have the well-mannered, well-dressed and intelligent youngster eager

to listen to his tales of public revenge carried out with the benign blessing of the law. Berry was so taken with the whole ritual that he even bought some of the old man's equipment from him. He could hardly wait to get the noose around someone's neck. When the Edinburgh Prison authorities were known to be looking for someone to step in and hang a couple of men sentenced to death by the courts, Berry, in spite of being the Public Executioner appointed by the Sheriff of London, wrote a sycophantic letter to them begging to be allowed to do the deed. As he said in his letter to the Magistrates of the City of Edinburgh:

Dear Sirs
I beg most respectfully to apply to you, to ask you if you will permit me to conduct the execution of the two convicts now lying under sentence of death at Edinburgh. I was very intimate with the late Mr Marwood and he made me thoroughly acquainted with his system of carrying out the work, and also the information which he learnt from the Doctors of different Prisons which he had to visit to carry out the last sentence of the law. I have now one rope of his which I bought from him at Horncastle, and have had two made from it. I also have two pinioning straps made from his, also two leg straps. I have seen Mr Calcraft execute three convicts at Manchester 13 years ago, and should you think fit to give me the appointment I would endeavour to merit your patronage. I have served eight years in Bradford and West Riding Police Force and resigned without a stain on my character and could satisfy you as to my abilities and fitness for the

appointment. You can apply to Mr James Withers, Chief Constable, Bradford, also to the High Sheriff of the City of London, Mr Clarence Smith, Mansion House Buildings, 4 Queen Victoria Street, London EC who will testify as to my character and fitness to carry out the Law. Should you require me I could be at your command at 24 hours notice. Hoping these few lines will meet with your approval,

I remain, Sirs,

Your most obedient servant,

James Berry.
PS An answer would greatly oblige as I should take it as a favour.

Is that high-class grovelling or what? Can you imagine the mind of a man who hangs around executions and even buys the memorabilia? What was he going to do with the grisly relics if he didn't get the job? Kidnap some poor sod off the street and practice on him? Luckily, the Edinburgh Magistrates decided to take him on so he was able to practice his sadistic tendencies within the law. And did he love it. He kept meticulous journals of each execution. Even down to what he had for dinner. He made a special memoir of the Edinburgh hanging.

'On Thursday March 27th 1884, I departed from my home, Bradford and made my way to Midland Station... I arrived at Waverley Station 4.20 pm and I hired a cab to drive me to the gaol... met at the doors by a good-looking warder... was confronted with the Governor, a very nice gentleman... as soon as I had washed and combed my hair, the tea was there... I sat down and enjoyed my first Scotch meal in Bonnie Scotland... I was escorted to my room... I then knelt down and asked the Almighty to help me in my most painful task... consisting of toast, ham and eggs and coffee... After that we paid another visit to the scaffold... After testing it with bags of cement... calculating the length of drop... I regretted for a while and then I thought about the public... I would not allow my feelings to overthrow me, so I never gave way to such thoughts again... 1pm I had my dinner... pudding, beef and vegetables, Scotch broth and Cochrane & Cantrell's ginger ale... After tea I had a chat with the warders... Another says, 'He looks a nice fellow for a job like that'... Saturday morning, 29th... After breakfast... I tested the scaffold... Vickers weighed 10 stones and over, 8 feet; and Innes, 9 stones, 10 feet drop... The rope was of Italian silk hemp... After dining... the reprieve was refused, the law was to take its course... I retired to bed as usual at 10 pm and after retiring said my prayers... where I only partook very sparingly of the nice and tempting ham and poached eggs put before me... My dinner did not arrive until 4 o'clock... consisting of rice pudding, black currants, chicken, vegetables, potatoes, bread and the usual teetotal beverages... I retired at 10... I was up and dressed at 5am... I fancied the ropes breaking... Breakfast had to be served earlier than usual... I made my way to the scaffold... The prisoners were brought face to face for the first time since their conviction... I was handed the warrant... I then proceeded to pinion the prisoners, previously shaking hands, bidding goodbye to this world. Both men seemed to feel the position very much. The procession was formed, headed by the High Bailiff, the Chaplain reading the litany for the dead. Both prisoners walked without assistance to the place of execution; they were at once placed under the beam on the drop where everything was done as quick as lightning, and both culprits paid the highest penalty of the law... The magistrates and doctors and even the press men, admitted that the execution of the two men had been carried out in as humane manner as possibly could be and the poor fellows had not suffered the slightest pain in going through the execution; doctors giving me testimonial as to the skilful way I had carried out the execution. 9am, my breakfast arrived…

Is this bloke enjoying himself or what? Exactly what is the difference between Berry and the run of the mill serial killer who can only get his pleasure from killing? From the way Berry details his feeding habits, it is clear that he feels that he is the star of the event. The two poor bastards are just the Magguffins to give the story legs. When it comes to the boring old bit of having to snatch the life away from the convicted murderers, he becomes brusque and eager to get back to his breakfast. He is really pleased that everybody was up there telling him what a wonderful job he had done. He was even given a testimonial by the prison surgeon which said that he had examined the dead bodies of the convicts Vickers and Innes and what a great job Berry had done making them that way.

At a later date, James Berry did put together a sort of apologia. He said that although they were great mates, Vickers and Innes were completely different from each other in character. They had both gone through a religious revival in the days leading up to the execution. Vickers was the eternal optimist and waited daily for a reprieve to arrive. Even when he was walking to the scaffold, he was still looking around as if someone would rush up waving a piece of paper and crying, 'Reprieve'. When he finally made the scaffold and had the noose adjusted around his neck, he suddenly realised the reality of his situation and promptly fainted. Innes took everything in his stride. He had protested his innocence at his trial because that was the thing to do. But there wasn't a lot of confidence in his protestations. Once the sentence had been passed, he accepted it and walked calmly to the scaffold.

Although considered highly skilled and technically excellent in the scientific art of dispatching the lawless,

Berry had an annus horriblis which he did not like to remember in his later years and hardly refers to it at all in his autobiography, *Life Story and Strange Experiences*. The year was 1886 when it all came unravelled. John Lee, the 'Man They Could Not Hang' was the first grain of grit in his toothpaste. Lee was accused of killing his employer because she made the miserly mistake of cutting his wages. To hide his crime he tried to burn down the house with her body in it. It was not effective and he faced the lonely 8am walk in Exeter jail in February. As he walked beside the Governor, he mentioned that he had dreamed that night that he would not hang. With respect to his circumstances, the Governor raised a polite eyebrow but need not suggest that perhaps the condemned man might be in an unhealthy state of denial. On the scaffold Berry went through his well-rehearsed, 17-second routine of manacling, pinioning and hooding his victim and then hauled on the lever. Nothing happened. Slightly embarrassed by his failure, Berry asked Lee to step aside while he had a look at the trap. Obligingly, Lee stood aside and waited. Berry tried the trap – it worked perfectly. Berry apologised for the delay and asked Lee to step back on to the trap. Which he did secure in the knowledge that his dream was about to become a fact. Again Berry pulled the lever – zilch. Lee was once again asked to step aside while Berry sent for some tools. With the observers looking on restlessly and Lee standing patiently by, Berry chiselled away at the woodwork until he was sure there would be no further foul-up. Politely, he once more asked Lee if he would mind stepping back on the trap and once again the noose was slipped around the neck of the condemned man. This time Barry almost tore the lever from its mounting in the effort to open the trap. Still it remained stubbornly shut. The Governor had seen enough. He ordered Lee back to his cell and ticked Berry off for wasting the taxpayers' money. No official reason was given for the non-functioning trap

and Magistrates were well aware of what could happen to a critic. One Senator foolish enough to criticise Caligula over a minor matter was invited to the palace. He was seized by a couple of Praetorian Guards and taken to the terrace which gave him an unrestricted view of the hills. There Caligula joined him and explained that it was not the fact that he had disagreed with him that had upset him. In fact, he quite liked to hear other people's views. The reason he was about to die was that he didn't like the way he wore his toga. Caligula then gave the signal for the executioner to take the Senator and sat on a seat where he could watch. The Senator was stripped of the offending toga and stretched out on a table. A woodsman was then brought in and ordered to saw the defenceless man in half. Caligula enjoyed the execution immensely. It was a brutal and painful way to kill a man but it was still within the bounds of what a strong, fun-loving ruler could get away with and still survive.

Caligula was then struck down with fever. He wasn't expected to live and the members of the Senate heaved a collective sigh of relief. Caligula's supporters, the Free Men of Rome, were not so happy. They were fully immersed in the entertainment their new-style Caesar insisted on providing for them. Rome came to a standstill. Work for half a mile around the palace was suspended. Horses and wagons were forbidden in the area. Day and night the crowd around the walls preyed silently for Caligula's recovery. One day he sat up and proclaimed that he hadn't been sick at all. What had actually happened was that he had been going through a metamorphosis. He was no longer merely a man with an exalted rank. Now, he was a God. The Senators waiting patiently at his bedside for him to expire, managed not to heave a sigh or raise an impious eyebrow. They hadn't been too enchanted with some of his actions as an imperial seigneur, they weren't looking forward to his actions not only as a Caesar but also a god. They were right

in their fears. Caligula's first action on his recovery was to declare yet another holiday. This one to honour his newly assumed divinity. He ordered his guards to go to the houses of his three sisters, get rid of their husbands and bring the girls to Rome. He had decided that as he was now divine, it must automatically mean that his sisters were the same – only on a lower level. It also occurred to him that it was only fitting that a God should consort with other Gods at a sexual level. Before long his siblings, Agrippinilla, Lesbia and Drusilla, were also sharing his bed. Not that he held his deity as a holy constriction on his liberal views. As a God he could make or break the rules. He chose to break them with great efficiency. With a group of mates of similar bents, he would maraud in disguise through the streets, stealing, wounding, raping as he went. One of his big turn-ons was to visit a brothel and after he and his guard had sampled the fruits, burn the place down.

It was about this time that events in the amphitheatres took an even nastier tone. Now he offered enormous purses to the Gladiators to fight to the death. A revolt by his chosen fighting men was put down by the army and bloody retribution visited on all those that had been involved. Now when they entered the ring, they knew that they wouldn't be coming out alive. If they won their first encounter, another man would be sent in. If the rebel won that, there would be another opponent sent out to kill him. If he continued to deny the Emperor and not die, he was stripped of armour and weapons and thrust back in with the menagerie of starving animals. One of the Senators summoned to attend Caligula in his box was foolish enough to show displeasure at the spectacle. Caligula was incensed. He called one of the gaolers from the cells under the arena and instructed him to dismember the fastidious Senator limb by limb. He sat impatiently waiting while his order was carried out and the mutilated body laid at his feet.

By this time Caligula was certifiably mad but

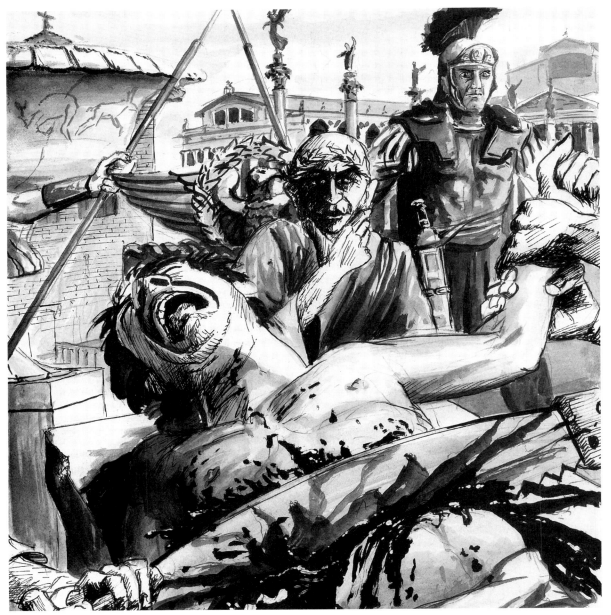

Caligula liked to see the blade cutting through the flesh when he had someone drawn in half.

there was nobody around in the position to sign the committal order. He still retained the loyalty of his officers and troops who had never had it so good. As long as a legionnaire declared his love of the Emperor, he could do no wrong. There were pockets of disquiet but these abruptly got quieter when Caligula's army of informers reported back to the boss. Although Caligula wouldn't listen to his advisers when they told him that the treasury was getting decidedly low on treasure, Caligula was no fool – only mad. Just feeding the lions fresh meat was an horrendous expense. But he was stoically prepared to bear it as long as the people cheered whenever he appeared and his God status was not in question. Unfortunately, lack of funds meant that the spectacles were getting less spectacular. The Gladiators were happy to go into the ring and slaughter each other when the purse could buy them more of whatever they wanted but inflation was biting as more and more finance was drained away from the treasury to satisfy Caligula's blood lust. This meant that the purse in their pocket was becoming rapidly worthless. So they did what dissatisfied soldiers have always done – they deserted. The outcome of this was that the circus became just a shabby replica of its former self. The bottom seemed to fall out of the business when the entertainment value was so bad that the fans actually jeered. Caligula couldn't believe what he was hearing. Those in the crowd who thought there was safety in numbers were soon to wish that they had thought again before showing their displeasure. A screaming Emperor sent his bully boys into the crowd to sort out the ring leaders. They wanted better entertainment – he would give them a show they would die for. He had the hecklers taken down to the vaults below the arena and had their tongues torn out with red-hot pincers. He ordered the animals to be let loose in the amphitheatre. In one inspired stroke, he solved the financially tedious problem of feeding the lions and tigers. It also had a salutary effect on the citizens. They suddenly realised that they were vulnerable. They saw the spectacle of their Emperor rolling around enjoying the sight of the tortured men being hunted and eaten and decided that perhaps it was funny after all.

On the home front, Caligula was having very messy affairs with his sisters – particularly Drusilla who was his favourite. When she became pregnant, he was over the moon. He couldn't wait to see his offspring – literally. After the problems with the citizenry at the Games, he decided he had to see his child, the new God, immediately. There were another three months to run on the pregnancy, too long for the obsessed Emperor. He strung Drusilla up and slit open her belly. When he found that the baby was dead, he attacked the dying women and hacked her to pieces. He then ate the baby. His argument was that it was a God so could not die – ergo if he ate it, he would assimilate that God as well and become even more divine. When a Senator had the temerity to point out that 'others' might not have the intelligence to take on board the Emperor's philosophical argument, he was ordered to go home and drink hemlock. But Caligula took his caution to heart and put out the story that his beloved sister had died from some hideous illness and her body was hastily cremated before anyone could see the awful mutilation of her body.

So it was back to the bloody circuses. Indiscriminate killing of the citizens could not go on. The more that were killed, the fewer there were to turn up for the revels. About this time, around AD 45, the Christians were beginning to be a recognisable sect in the city. They were preaching that there was only one God and that everyone was equal in His sight. Anathema to Caligula. If they were espousing another deity, where did that leave him? He solved yet another problem with the brilliant skill of a true entrepreneur. Feeding the animals was the problem. He couldn't go on using the Free Men so – he decreed that Christianity was an abomination. Christians must be eliminated. What better way than by using them as fodder for the animals? They could also be pressed into service for other things. Nailed to the cross, soaked in tar and planted on the roads leading to the arena, they could be used as torches. Even better, their property could be sequestered to the uses of the State. He spread his net wider. He promised gold to anyone who brought evidence of sedition against his neighbour. He wasn't too choosy about how good the evidence was. If it could be proved that an informer had given forced evidence, he could either be used as lion meat or, if he had an estate, he could be butchered and his wealth turned over to Caligula. Still the orgies went on. When he was just little 'little boots', a fortune teller had predicted that he had as much chance of being Emperor as he had of walking across the Bay of Naples without getting his sandals wet. Remembering the boyhood put-down, he had 4000 boats built and collected in the bay. They were tied together and Caligula led a raiding party across the pontoon bridge to pillage the town of Puteoli on the far side. Excited by his cunning coup of combining a revisionist's view of his fate and the sacking of a town that had been given him problems, he was not amused when he was awakened in the night with the news that the ships he had used to bridge the gap had been caught up in a mighty storm and most of them had been sent to the bottom. It was not what he wanted to hear. He swore a terrible oath that he would make Neptune the King of the sea pay for the affront he had made to his person. But that still didn't sort out the problem of the empty coffers in the treasury. He then had the tremendous idea of turning the palace into a high-class brothel. An authority on brothels, he decided that instead of the men with the money wasting it in the private enterprise whorehouses, they could come to the palace and help support the state. As an added bonus, he ordered that his divine surviving sisters, Agrippinilla and Lesbia, should be used as special bait. After all it was not

every day that the fans got a chance to have intercourse with a Goddess. It had to be worth a lot more than what was being charged by the common courtesans and prostitutes. He was not happy when nobody turned up to savour his largesse. They had ample examples of Caligula's sense of humour and they were not looking for more trouble. Caligula was furious. So he sent out the invitation again. This time it was not possible to refuse. There was no RSVP. Well they could, theoretically, refuse but even if they did they were expected to pay the massive cover charge that Caligula levied on all his paying guests. Just to make sure that they all got the point that Caesar was making, they were also ordered to make their daughters available at the orgies. This, as you may assume, was not the most popular decree Caligula had ever made. It confirmed to the Senators that Caligula really was mad. There is nothing like being in the firing line to get generals wanting to finish the war. They wanted to get rid of him but while he might be mad, bad and extremely unhealthy to know, he was not stupid. He was short of money but there was always enough to keep the officers of his bodyguard sweet. The Senators began to meet secretly. Sometimes not secretly enough. Caligula's paid goons were everywhere and just the hint of sedition was enough to get the death penalty. If the culprit was lucky, by his own hand. The unlucky ones were subjected to Caligula's torturers and then either strangled, crucified or fed to the lions. The main problem for the Senators was that their chosen Caesar had been chosen for life. There was no small print that said if they didn't like him they could get rid of him or that they could in any way censure his activities. And Caligula knew it. There wasn't even the possibility of bringing in a contender and letting the two of them slug it out. Livia, Caligula's great grandmother, had seen to that. Anyone who represented the smallest threat to his ascension to the throne had been systematically slaughtered – even her own husband Augustus had been fed the poisoned grapes when it appeared that he was over-fond of his grandson, Agrippa. Just to make sure, she got rid of the grandson as well. But all her efforts to put her son Tiberius on the throne and live in his reflected glory came to nought. He couldn't stand her and rather than stay in the same country he went to live on the Isle of Capri. It hurt Livia but she soon recovered and before long it was Livia that was running the mighty Roman Empire. She was so powerful that nobody tried to point out that she wasn't the Caesar they were all sworn to obey. The Caesar they were all sworn to obey was living it up in his island retreat. Tiberius rapidly became the debaucher's debaucher. When Livia finally died, he refused to come to Rome for the funeral. The scuttlebutt was that he was so degenerated by his years of debauchery that he didn't want anyone to see him. The real reason was possibly that he couldn't stand his mother when she was alive and now, in his 80s, he wasn't going to take the hideously uncomfortable road to Rome to visit her in death. It was against this background of family discord that Caligula, an unlikely outsider for the laurels at birth, came to be the undisputed leader. And the reason why the Senators found themselves unable to do anything about the status quo.

A new wheeze struck Caligula. He was sure that there were still untapped sources of finance and that it was only being withheld from him by mean-minded landowners and Senators to spite him. He ordered all the men of property to meet him in Lyons and to bring their money with them. When they arrived they were given a welcoming banquet and told the reason for the little get together. They were being given the marvellous opportunity of buying some of the treasures of the Empire at a knockdown price. To make it interesting for them, he would make the bids for them. To help them carry away the wonderful bargains they were about to acquire, he was giving them the services of his battle-trained army. They

got the point. By the end of the 'auction', the 'bidders' were broke and the auctioneer rich. What was even better, as far as Caligula was concerned, was that the 'artefacts' he had sold were more by way of being 'memorabilia'. Old sandals, a threadbare toga or two, and any old junk culled from the palace attic that had seen better days.

Casting around for more ways of eeking out an Imperial living he decided to push on through France and Germany collecting from the various leaders of communities that held their position through the Roman administration. He finished up on the north coast of France. Just a few short miles from Britain. He had originally intended to pay the Brits an unscheduled visit. Within sight of the white cliffs of Dover he had a change of mind. He wanted to go home. He called in the captains of his army and told them his decision. They were not happy. They had come a long way with their capricious boss, acting as tax collectors and general bully boys. Now they wanted to do something as soldiers. A trip to Britain to help discipline the surly Brits would do a lot for their morale. As usual when he wasn't obeyed instantly, Caligula flew into a rage. He ordered the Army to be assembled in full combat gear. He left them standing in full armour until just before sunset then rode out on his favourite horse, Incitatus, which he had recently ennobled with the title of Consul, and led them to the beach. He drew his sword, stood in the stirrups and pointed at the gently breaking waves. There was the enemy – King Neptune. He reminded them of how Neptune had wrecked his ships in the Bay of Naples. Now was the time for revenge. He then ordered the cavalry to charge. They, at first thought he was joking. He soon disabused them of that erroneous thought. They charged into the water, cutting about them with their swords. Then Caligula ordered in the infantry. He rushed among them, laying about with his sword if he thought anyone was attacking Neptune with anything less than total commitment. When it got dark he called a halt and declared that he had won the battle.

Now he was master of the seas. And as the Victor he would take the Victor's tribute. He ordered all the men, officers included, to gather up the spoils of the sea and pack them so that they could be transported back to Rome in triumph. This little display of temper that had reduced the proud Roman legionnaires to acting like idiots and the muttering in the ranks was increased by the long, forced march back to Rome. Caligula had had enough of foreign adventures and wanted the comfort of his own home. He was aware that there were elements in his army that were the whole 110% that he demanded. He wasn't worried. While the Imperial Guard was in the hands of Cassius Charea, he was safe. It was Charea who had given him his little soldier uniform and the sobriquet of 'Little Boots'. Once back in Rome, Charea would root out any dissension in the ranks, they could have a really interesting circus with real soldiers fighting to the death, and everything would be right with his world. When Cassius Charea was approached by other officers about an insurrection in the ranks, he warned them not to try anything or they would have to answer to him. But even Charea's staunch support of the Emperor was sorely tested on their entry into Rome. The entire expedition had been a meaningless foible. Even the money they had exacted from the French and Germans hadn't been enough to pay the outstanding wages of the army. Caligula was treating it as if he had just won a magnificent military campaign. His arrival in Rome was laid on as a treat for a conquering hero. Caligula arrived with a handful of German villagers, a couple of Britains and massive panniers of seashells. The citizens turning out to watch the parade didn't exactly laugh, they knew better, but the welcome was somewhat less than overwhelming. And Caligula still needed money. He called in Charea and made a fatal mistake. The old boy was up for almost anything as long as he kept a modicum of dignity. He had looked on with dismay at the antics on the French coast but as he hadn't been expected to pick up seashells, he let it pass. Caligula now wanted him to go out and collect taxes, which he was not prepared to do. He now began to listen to the soft words of treason breathed by his fellow officers and when he was approached by two senators, he was ripe for plucking. Cornelius Sabinus and Arrecinus Clemens had been favoured by Caligula and had not suffered some of the indignities suffered by others of their rank. They had even complied with his order to present their daughters at the Imperial Whorehouse. But they sensed that now, after the ridiculous 'French Campaign', the Emperor's strength was weakened. They approached Charea cautiously, knowing the soldier's great affection for his Emperor. They were grateful to find him open to the ideas they gently broached.

Once Charea had made up his mind, he wanted action. He, more than anyone, knew Caligula's routine. He waited outside one of the popular playhouses and when he saw Caligula come out on to the balcony at the end of the play, he approached him. He didn't waste time in formal greetings. He just drew his sword and ran the Emperor through. He watched as his young master died at his feet, then strode into the theatre and announced that, due to the sudden death of Caesar, the entertainment was over.

18
Major Otto Dickmann

The reason for picking out Otto Dickmann as the one responsible for what happened on a beautiful summer's day in the little village of Oradour-sur-Glane is purely arbitrary. Although nobody has been able to assess with certainty the reason for the massacre, there are dozens of theories. Usually it is accepted that it was in revenge for general French Resistance activity in the area. It is true that a couple of German lorries were ambushed and their cargo stolen only a few miles from the village two days earlier. It was rumoured the lorries carried a vast amount of Nazi gold. The reason the Nazis had committed it to the dangers of the open road was the Allied invasion in Normandy. It was destined for the greater security that Germany would, hopefully, be able to offer. It is further rumoured that the Resistance fighters were overwhelmed by the treasure they discovered on board and a gun battle ensued from which only one man survived. He is said to have single-handedly buried the gold and got away. Again, rumour has it that he went to live in Switzerland and in the 1980s returned to the Limoges area and retrieved some of the gold. He then tried to get several banks interested in retrieving the rest. An Englishmen sent to investigate was arrested and spent several years in prison. The reason this story seems a bit dubious is not that the ambush seems improbable, similar raids were happening all the time, but that one man, or even 10 men, could have shifted and hidden the amount of gold claimed to have been in the lorries in such a short space of time. What's more, hidden it so well that thousands of treasure hunters since have never been able to pinpoint its whereabouts. In reality, the cause of the massacre was much simpler.

The Second Panzer Division, known as Das Reich, had expected to be sent north to help repel the Allied invasion forces. Hitler had decreed that they should remain in the south of France because he expected the Allies to at least make a secondary landing on the south-west coast. If the Das Reich SS Division had been moved to try to stem the advance of the Allies, the result of the invasion might have been quite different. It is even possible that it might have pushed the invaders back into the sea. If they had done that, it would have been a long time before another force capable of forcing a beach head could have been mustered. It would have prolonged the war by at least two years and there is a strong possibility that Oradour would have been spared. The Division was the strongest in the German army at that time and it is still a mystery to military leaders why Hitler chose to keep it in reserve. It had air reconnaissance units, tanks of all types from armoured troop carriers to heavy assault tanks, modern anti-aircraft guns and dozens of support units of all sorts. Unlike a lot of the Divisions actually engaging the enemy, the Das Reich Division also had a plentiful supply of fuel. It is true that the Division had just suffered massive losses on the Eastern Front and had hardly escaped annihilation as a fighter group. But during their sojourn in south-west France they had been rejoined by the Second Artillery Panzer Regiment, the Third Grenadier

Major Dickman sought revenge for the disappearance of his friend by burning the village of Oradour to the ground and murdering all its inhabitants.

Panzer Regiment, known as Das Deutschland, and the Fourth Grenadier Panzer Regiment, Der Führer. To bring them up to strength after the wastage of the Russian campaign, the units had been freshly supplied with recruits from other sources. Many of them were young and badly trained. There was a large intake of conscripts from Alsace, a region that had been French until the Nazis had redefined the boundaries of the Third Reich in 1940. These youngsters were suffering a crushing insecurity problem and tended to expiate it on their former compatriots. They were about to get their chance. SS General Heinz Lammerding received news that the German garrison in Tulle had been attacked with considerable loss of life. Major Wulf and Major Dickmann were happy to have something to do. They rode into Tulle at the head of a large motorised column and proceeded to round up anyone they came across. They set up a command post in the square and set the troops to sacking the town. Then they took the men they had picked up and hanged them on the lamp posts along the main avenue. Orders had been sent out to all units from Lammerding to the effect that 'every effort must be made to destroy the Resistance network and that reprisals should be taken against civilian populations encouraging, aiding their endeavours or harbouring Resistance criminals.' It was an open invitation to murder. More residents of the fated town would have been strung up but it was a lengthy business and tedious trying to get it right without co-operation from the victims. The rest of the citizenry was rounded up and deported as slave labour to the badly damaged towns of the Ruhr valley. Many of these would die in the massive bombing raids that were carried out by the RAF and USAF on the industrial areas of central Germany.

Once the fury of the assault on Tulle had been unleashed it was a hard beast to cage. Two days later Dickmann and his Der Führer Regiment received orders that they were to be moved up towards the front. Hitler had at last listened to his Generals. He had wanted to reserve his crack Panzer units to hit the enemy at a later date. He was afraid that if he committed them and they were blown away by the opposing forces, the German army would have nothing to fall back on. It took a long time for his advisors to get across the point that the longer he held the tanks back, the stronger the opposition would be. The time to strike was now. Hot news was that the beach heads in Normandy had been consolidated and the Allies were heading south. Another piece of news, for Major Dickmann, was more personal. A friend of Dickmann's, Major Kämpfe was missing, believed to be a prisoner of the Resistance – possibly already executed. Dickmann was on the road that led close to Oradour. It was a small, idyllic village beside a tree-lined river. It had never caught the attention of the German Army before. It had no strategic value and no nightlife. It did have a small restaurant. When the Panzers had first moved into the area, Dickmann and Kämpfe had spent many happy hours touring around the countryside. They had been taken with Oradour's rural charm and had visited the restaurant on several occasions. It was unfortunate that Dickmann heard the news of his friend's death while he was in the Oradour area. He remembered with bitterness the welcome the villagers had given them and now they were party to his friend's murder. He decided to make an example of the village.

It was lunchtime on a warm summer's day in 1944, June 10th, to be exact. Those that weren't working in the fields or away in the surrounding towns shopping were sitting in the warm sunlight eating lunch. They weren't particularly disturbed when Der Führer Regiment moved into town. They had heard about the hangings in Tulle but supposed that there was some substance in the claim that the citizens had been aiding the Resistance. They didn't feel they were in any danger. Their attitude had been – if the Boche didn't disturb them – they wouldn't disturb the Boche. They did get a little concerned when Dickmann ordered his men to round everyone up and gather them in the area outside the church. Only one small boy escaped the net. He was an evacuee from Alsace and was terrified of the Germans. He ran out to the fields and told the labourers what was happening. They didn't know what to do so they did nothing. For sure there was nothing they could do but get themselves killed. Once Dickmann was sure that he had the undivided attention of the villagers, he told them that he had been given information that there were Resistance workers in the village. The villagers protested but Dickmann was not in listening mode. He told them that as they were being uncooperative and not volunteering the information he needed, he would search the village until he found what he wanted. For over an hour the troops scoured the village, smashing, stealing, destroying. When Dickmann was satisfied that there was nothing else of value to be had, he ordered his men to separate the people. Men were to be locked in the barns and women and children in the church. The church was small and hardly adequate for the 245 women and 207 children held there. The 190 men confined to the barns were hardly better off. For the next hour the soldiers went through the village setting fire to anything that would burn. While all this mayhem was being unleashed, a woman who had been visiting her daughter-in-law in Limoges returned. She was stopped by the guard on the bridge over the river. He told her that the village was out of bounds. She argued with him, demanded to see his superior officer. The soldier stood firm, refused to let her cross the bridge. She was finally persuaded to leave.

The village was destroyed but still Dickmann wasn't satisfied. He watched as his men reassembled outside the church. Around them the scene was Dantean. The roar of flames as they consumed the buildings, the crash as roofs collapsed and the screams and pleas of the terrified women in the church made the sunny afternoon hideous. Dickmann stood in the back of his staff car and called his men to attention. His orders made even the brutalised soldiers look at each other in disbelief. He told them to torch the church and shoot anyone trying to escape. When they hesitated, he reminded them what happened to soldiers who failed to obey a direct order in war time. The soldiers gathered together as much straw, wood and other inflammable materials as they could find and soaked them in petrol. Then they got several cans of fuel and rolled them into the church. The women began to get the idea of just what the Nazis were capable of and stormed the door. They were driven back by machine gun fire. Those killed in the vicious attack were the lucky ones. The Nazi troops pushed the inflammable material into the church and piled it up at the doors and windows. When the torch was put to it, the whole building was alight in seconds. At each door and window a machine gun crew was positioned with its lethal weapons targeting the opening. Inside the women ran around, tried to find a way out. In desperation many tried to leap through the flame only to be met by a hail of bullets as, their clothes and hair on fire, they touched the ground. At last part of the roof collapsed and brought a merciful end to the 452 women and children trapped inside. Through it all Dickmann watched from the back of his staff car, untouched by the horrendous crime that was being committed in front of him and on his orders.

Now Dickmann turned his attention to the men of the village. He had no problem getting his men to carry out his instructions this time. The crime that they had committed would damn them for eternity

The women and children were burned alive in the church.

and in their hearts they knew there was no redemption. The doors of the barns were thrown open and the machine gunners directed a deadly stream of fire at the men huddled within. Then, when there was no more movement in the barn, with typical Teutonic thoroughness, Dickmann had the barns set alight. The troops retired to the road that runs into the village and silently watched it burn. There were no more screams. Just the flames lighting the sky as the sun set and the occasional distant crash as another house collapsed. Dickmann seemed loathed to leave the village. As if the evilness that he had unleashed there was tying him to the spot. He ordered the cooks to prepare a feast for the troops using the food and wine they had confiscated from the 'Resistance'. Some of the soldiers went and sat by the river and thought dark thoughts. Others took advantage of the relaxation of discipline and tried to drink away the memories of the screams and the chatter of machine guns directing a deadly hail of bullets into the unarmed villagers. Dickmann's actions were more chilling. With only the glow from the embers to light his way, he walked slowly through the carnage he had created, his pistol drawn, shooting at any of the bodies he thought might still possess a breath of life. The crack of his pistol was heard late into the night. In the surrounding fields those lucky enough to avoid the slaughter laid low. They didn't want to draw attention to themselves by going into what remained of the village. The next day the Panzer Regiment left. Only the still smouldering remains of the village bore witness to the mindless carnage that had taken place in three short hours.

It wasn't until the third day after the massacre that anyone went into the village. Unbelievably they found three men still alive. They were badly injured but were able to describe to the world what happened on that hot June afternoon in graphic detail.

The Das Reich Division were at last given orders to engage the enemy. What the more astute Waffen SS Generals had predicted was found to be true. Once a beach head had been established and supply lines secured the Allied forces were unstoppable. Major Otto Dickmann was burned to death when his staff car was strafed by an Allied fighter plane. Major Kämpfe, who was the alleged cause of the incident, was never heard of again. No Resistance unit claimed to have kidnapped him and his body was not recovered. With all the villagers dead, there was no point in reconstructing the ancient village. It was decided to leave it as the neighbours found it when they went to see what had happened there. Visiting the village on a sunny afternoon, walking passed the shell of the church, looking into the empty houses with sewing machines and rotting furniture still in place, passing the burned out, rusting little cars and the wrecked, old-fashioned bicycles it is hard to believe that it isn't just a film set waiting for the director, the cameraman and the actors to take up their positions.

But it did happen – and the shame of it will never be forgotten.

19
Andrei Chikatilo

America makes a strong claim to be voted the serial killer centre of the world. In recent years England hasn't done too badly and France has also put in a strong bid. Germany even managed to turn serial killing into a government policy in the Thirties and Forties. But the Eastern Block put up a murderer who will take some beating. Before the Soviet Union decided to go back to its old title of Russia, very little news of a domestic nature managed to ooze over the Iron Curtain. They may have killed millions from starvation and the Gulags could give the Gestapo lessons on sheer indifference but this was considered not to be something of international importance. Besides, the Soviets were a paradise and the governors were principled men who knew what was right for the people. Having an Andrei Chikatilo on the books wasn't something they were going to boast about to the degenerate West. That Chikatilo was a victim of Stalin's manic determination to farm the steppes of Russia under the unworkable Workers Collective Farming Scheme, is undeniable. This was the cause of the death of millions of farm workers in the area of the Ukraine where Andrei was born. Peasants who tried to hide crops from the collectors were bayoneted to death or sent to Siberia to labour in the freezing climate with no real hope of ever being released. Even the seed corn was collected by the ignorant, city-born Soviet agents who failed to realise that if the farmers had no seeds for the next year's crop there would be no harvest. This was one of the main causes of the famine. Andrei hadn't been the first born to his parents. They had an older child, Stephan, who

had succumbed to malnutrition when he was three years old. He had been eaten by the starving neighbours. Cannibalism was a thing of necessity. Burying a body in the ground served nobody's interest. These harsh conditions were directly responsible for breeding the murderer Andrei Chikatilo. The chronic malnutrition suffered by his parents corrupted his genes and left him with slight hydrocephalus, one eye not fully developed and genital and urinary tract malformations. In spite of this, he was intelligent and ready to learn. When he was just a boy, he decided that the education he was receiving at his primary school wasn't good enough. He wrote a precocious letter to the Central Communist Education Committee and complained. Khrushchev had decreed that every Soviet child should be educated according to his or her ability and, he claimed, his ability was far in advance of that of his classmates. His boldness paid off and he was put into an institute for high achievers. It meant long periods away from home but he didn't mind that too much. The family, Andrei, his sister Tatiana and their parents, lived in a one-bedroomed flat with only cold water. It was typical accommodation for a family that had come to the big city to make a fortune only to find that the citizens had already got control of what he was looking for. He found the town's children were a lot more hostile than those in his Ukrainian village. His eyesight was bad and this meant he was ragged constantly about his 'four eyes'. He had a weak, lanky body and his lack of co-ordination made him useless at sports. His accent didn't help much either. But he was clever. Another reason for his

Andrei Chikatilo was put in a cage at his trial to defend him from the relatives of the children he had murdered. (EPA Photo)

contemporaries to give him a bad time. What was more, he always seemed to be ill. Home was no shelter from the constant bullying. His father was away fighting the Germans for much of Andrei's early life, so he was left to the mercy of his frustrated mother. She had a theory, common among mothers at that time, that children were inherently stupid and the only way to get through to them was by shouting. Shouting and the delivery of stinging blows to the head whenever the child was in range. It was difficult for Andrei to keep out of range. There was only one bed in the flat and he slept in it with his mother. He also had a weak bladder as well as a genital malformation. The weak bladder assured that he started each day with a beating from his mother when she found the bed clothes sodden. The genital deformation at this time was no real problem. His mother was a typical peasant woman with a deep-seated distrust of doctors and anyone who could write. When Tatiana was born she had a prolapsed colon. It is not uncommon when the mother has not been used to a healthy diet. Neither is it particularly dangerous. Most mothers would have pointed it out to the doctor or mid-wife and the little tube of flesh would have been popped back in safely. Andrei was made to stand and watch while his mother performed the procedure herself. The obvious pain and the blood made a lasting impression on the boy and he was never able to look at his sister without remembering what had happened.

At school Andrei was making good grades in spite of his, at times, nightmarish home life. His father was back from the war and it hadn't improved him. Now Andrei had to put up with not only constant abuse from his mother but abuse and physical violence from his father as well. When they weren't having a go at him, they were slamming into each other. It was a miracle that Andrei was able to keep up with his schoolwork at all. And he had another problem. While all his classmates had been blessed with falling testicles, a breaking voice and erotic dreams of female conquest, all Andrei could manage was a wet bed. The only

excitement he got was from seeing blood. He didn't mind whose it was. If no one else was willing to contribute, he was willing to supply his own. Much of his reading was about the war. The more graphic and bloody the better. He found security in working for the Communist party. If there was a rally going and posters needed to be painted, Andrei was there. He was a good artist and found some satisfaction in the pride of producing graphic designs that other, more active members of the party, took on marches.

By the time he was 16, he was having real psychological problems. These were mainly brought on by the terrifying fact that his sexual organs were not functioning as they should. He still hadn't had an erection and had begun desperately to seek some method to achieve it. The nearest he ever came to an orgasm was when blood was involved and he knew that it was wrong. He needed actual sexual experience but any girl he came into contact with made it very obvious that she thought he was a nerd. Not a reaction to build confidence in a spotty-faced, weak-bodied, bed-wetting, myopic adolescent. But he did try.

His sister had a friend about her own age, 10 or 11, who would come to play outside the block of flats. Sometimes when it was raining the girls were allowed in as long as they didn't make a noise and kept out of the way of Mama Chikatilo. When Andrei came home from school one day, he found that his mother and sister had gone to the shops leaving the little girl alone. Being alone with the innocent girl made Andrei feel ill. He tried to talk to her but couldn't think of anything to say. Without a word he grabbed her and wrestled her to the floor. He grappled at her, clumsily tried to push his finger into her vagina. She fought desperately. Andrei was so aroused that he had his first ejaculation. It hit him like a thunderbolt. As he sat dazed, trying to calm his trembling body, the girl managed to jump up and run away. He was still sitting there when her father arrived and beat him up. Andrei didn't mind. He rather enjoyed the pain. It fitted in with his new and mind-blowing sexual experience. Not only had he been able to run his hands over the female body but he had now learned that he could have an orgasm. He began to look around for other conquests. In spite of his sexual awakening and his preoccupation with sexual matters, his academic work was still of such a high standard that he was encouraged to take the examination for the Faculty of Law at Moscow University. There was only one problem as far as he could see and he brought it to the attention of the authorities. The entrance exam was in Russian and he was a Ukrainian speaker by birth and would therefore be at a disadvantage. He was assured that this would be taken into consideration. It pleased Andrei to have achieved that small victory. It wasn't really a valid argument. He had had no problems to date with working in the Russian language. The results of his examination were disappointing. He passed with good grades but was not offered a place at the prestigious Moscow State University. This was another humiliation. He put it down to the fact that his parents were not party members and his father hadn't exactly distinguished himself in the war against Germany. Andrei didn't care what the reason was – it was just another instance of his unworthiness. Instead of going to one of the lesser universities, he enrolled in a Polytechnic to study communications. It wasn't what he wanted but he did it in an effort, at least in his own mind, to 'show them'. Intellectually it was not stimulating and he was happy to finish the course and didn't complain too much when he was drafted into the forces. His time in the forces was yet another time of humiliation and degradation. He was picked on by his peers and bullied by his superiors. The country surrounding the camp boasted neither entertainment, nor female company. The only time he tried to chat up one of the women soldiers, he was mortified to hear that she had told his colleagues of his clumsy attempts to date her. He couldn't wait to get out of the army. His first action as a civilian was to apply for, and get, Party Membership. With his enhanced status he moved into better accommodation. He was

extremely proud of this and when Tatiana was 18 and left school he invited her to come and live with him. She was happy to get away from her chaotic and brutal home life and accepted the invitation with alacrity. She stayed with him for six months. It was one of the happiest times of his life. He fussed over her, wouldn't allow her to cook or do any of the housework and encouraged her to meet new friends. Which she did. Vasily, a labourer. Andrei didn't think he was good enough for her but he made her happy so he gave the marriage his blessing. In gratitude, Tatiana found him a wife, Feodosia Odmachewa. Within a month of their first meeting, Andrei and Feodosia were married. His wife's family were very happy with the match. He was an intellectual, read a lot, didn't drink and was a paid-up member of the Party. Feodosia turned out to be a civilised version of his mother. She also believed that shouting delivered results. Chikatilo was calmed by his new status. He decided that there was a possibility of improving his status now that he was a Party member and took up a course at the Rostov State University. He got a degree in literature in 1970. He was now, officially, an intellectual. Through the good offices of an acquaintance, he was offered the post of deputy director and teacher of Russian literature at a school in Nowoshakhtinsk. He was not a success. He was too shy and un-streetwise to gain any authority over the students. Instead, he began to rant about the sexual activities of his students. From just complaining about it he went to spying. He hung around the ladies toilets and fantasised some improbable scenarios. Soon watching wasn't enough. He got one of his girl pupils to stay behind and then attacked her. She started screaming and he ran off. She reported him to the head and he was asked to leave. It didn't worry him particularly. He had managed to get his hand into her blouse for a couple of seconds and the thrill of the feel still lingered. In spite of this attack, he was able to walk straight into another job as a teacher. Without the damning report of the molestation on his curriculum, it was easy. He was a married man with two children, a degree from a top university and had that all important qualification – membership of the Party. His sexuality had always been on the fragile side but now it seemed to jump a cog or two. He enticed a couple of children back to his apartment on the pretext of donating some books to their school. As soon as he got them alone he tried to get them to put their hands inside his trousers. The girls thought it was a bit of a giggle but ran off when he tried to take their clothes off. They reported the encounter to their parents but were told not to make up such stories. Why would an educated man like Comrade Chikatilo do a thing like that? Andrei was getting more confident with every encounter. Nobody had taken the reported attacks seriously and he still had his job. But he had to be careful. He bought a little place in the poor part of town. It wasn't much, no sanitation or water but it suited him. He was able to entice some of the gypsy girls down there and vent some of his frustration on them. Then he met 10-year-old Yelena Zakotnowa. He was walking near the little hovel he had recently bought when he saw Yelena a few steps ahead of him carrying a big bag of vegetables in her arms. He offered to carry them for her. She was happy to be rid of the burden. They were walking along a little used path with bushes and tall grass on either side. As Chikatilo talked to the child he suddenly had an overwhelming desire to touch her naked body. He looked carefully around. Nobody about. He dropped the vegetables and picked up the girl and tossed her into the bushes. She tried to scream but he roughly put his hand around her throat. He tore off her knickers and scrabbled at her vagina. He laid on top of her now motionless body and ejaculated onto her stomach. Exhausted he sat back and pulled his clothes around his sweating body. For the first time he took in that the girl was dead. Suddenly, he hated her, hated her for what she had made him become. Her eyes were open, staring at him. He ripped a piece of cloth from her dress and wrapped it around her head so that those accusing eyes were hidden. In fury, he pulled out his pocket knife and fell on the tiny body. Repeatedly, he

stabbed in the belly, the chest, the womb. Exhausted, he pulled her clothing back into place and threw the body into the river running close behind the bushes. The bag of vegetables followed. When the body of little Yelena was found the police threw out a wide net and found Chikatilo. It was thought strange that he, an intellectual, a member of the Party, should have accommodation in that area. He had a ready explanation. Now that his father was a widower, Andrei had thought to buy him a place of his own. The little cabin was going cheap so he bought it. Unfortunately, his father didn't like the area so he was stuck with the hovel on his hands and was hoping to unload it on a buyer. The police were satisfied and turned their attention elsewhere. They soon came up with another suspect who wasn't so versatile with the truth. The police manufactured enough evidence against him to put him in front of a firing squad. Another crime to be removed from the blotter. And a confidence booster for Chikatilo. He felt invincible. Maybe he couldn't get what he wanted by gentle persuasion but he had found, for him, a better way of satisfying his sexual urges.

He began to prowl the streets at night. At a bus stop on a dark night in December he saw a teenage girl trying to get a lift. She wasn't getting anywhere. Chikatilo approached her and offered to buy her a bus ticket. She told him to get lost. He moved off and hung around as if waiting for a bus. Still the girl couldn't get any customers. After a while she came over to Chikatilo and asked him if he wanted to buy her a drink. He bought her a beer and asked if she wanted to earn some money. She led him across the road and into some trees. He was desperate to have a normal sexual experience. The girl slipped off her knickers, hitched up her skirt and leant back against a tree. Chikatilo tried desperately to get an erection. The girl got bored and dropped her skirt. It wasn't her fault he couldn't get it on – she wanted paying just the same. Chikatilo begged her to let him try again. She laughed and turned to go. Chikatilo grabbed her by the throat and pinned her against the tree. He pulled out his knife and stabbed her in the vagina then, as she fell to the ground in agony he dropped on her, stabbing, ripping off her clothes. Gaping wounds gushed blood, he silenced her whimpers with a savage slash across her throat. He pulled himself on top of her and simulated the motion of the sex act, revelling in the feel of the hot blood on his skin. Finally, he reached the orgasm he craved. In delirium, he stabbed at his victim's eyes, gouging them from the sockets. He stumbled from the wood and made his way to the bus stop. There was a small lamp there and by its light he saw that he was covered in blood. He slunk back into the darkness and scrubbed his top coat on the ground until all traces of blood were gone. He calmly took the next bus back to town.

This became Chikatilo's modus operandi. He would meet a girl, entice her somewhere it was unlikely that they would be disturbed – then attack. There was nothing planned or clever about his attacks. He began to get more adept but the operation remained the same. Another girl that he took into the woods taunted him because he couldn't get an erection. He didn't let her die quickly. Slowly and with great relish he slit open her breasts, pierced her windpipe, sliced open her belly and thrust down through her sex organs. When she was dead, he masturbated over the body and then bit off her nipples and ate parts of her internal organs. It was a long-lasting orgasm and he couldn't get enough of it. He didn't care who it was that fell victim to his abnormal desires. He picked up a young boy outside a shop. He found out that the youngster was interested in stamps and asked him back to his place to see his collection. He led the way through a park. The boy followed happily. When Chikatilo was sure that he was not observed, he dragged the boy into the bushes. His attempts at sodomy where unsuccessful so he cut off the boy's penis. He dispatched the mutilated child with a deep cut across the windpipe and finished up with his trademark – the stab in each eye. He sat with the boy for a long time, watching the blooded seep from the

wounds and gradually cease to flow. He licked the blood from the wounds and then ate the testicles. At last he was satisfied. He dropped the boy's clothes over his ravaged face and went home to his wife.

Now that Chikatilo had got the hang of it, he couldn't stop. At least once a week he went on the prowl. He wasn't always successful. When he was, he went through the same routine each time. He took the mark to a suitably isolated location, killed either by cutting his victim's windpipe or by strangling and then cutting the windpipe. He would then mutilate the body. Girls would have their nipples cut off and he would eat them. Then he would mutilate the vagina, cut pieces off and then eat them. This would usually bring him to a state of orgasm. He would eject his semen on to the body and then lap up the blood from the wounds like an animal. Boys suffered a similar fate. While they were still alive, he would cut off their penis and catch the blood in his mouth as it spurted from the severed artery. After the kill, he would cut out and eat the testicles. Unlike most serial killers, he had no compulsion to take away a souvenir of his ghastly crime. It was the simplicity of his murders that kept him safe. He never planned anything and never took anything from the scene of the crime.

Occasionally, something did go wrong but he had the wit to circumvent any disaster. Like the time he invited a boy back to his daughter's flat to see some special videos. The flat was empty. Chikatilo's daughter had recently married and moved away leaving the flat for her brother. He was serving in the Russian forces in Afghanistan at the time. The boy came innocently. Chikatilo gave him a lemonade and sat him on the sofa to watch the television. He waited for a while, watched the boy's happy face watching the videos. Then he went to the kitchen, picked out a large knife and came up behind the boy and cut his throat. Chikitalo carried out his accustomed ritual of necromancy and mutilation and then, for the first time sat back and realised what he had done. Here, there was no convenient stream or wood to hide the body. If he left it in the flat, it would be discovered when his son returned. Chikatilo looked around the blood-stained flat and realised he had made a big mistake. He needed to cover it up before daylight. He wrapped the body in a blanket then systematically went about mopping up the blood. Next, he took the body into the tiny bathroom and hacked it into small pieces, which he tied into the blanket. It was a pathetically small bundle but too large to risk walking through the streets carrying it on his back at night. He needed to get to his dumping ground in the forest. He went out into the night to try to find a vehicle of some sort. In a front garden he found a sledge. Quietly, he pulled it out on the road and hurried back to the flat. He put the body on the sledge and covered it with boxes and pieces of old sacking. His intention was to make for the woods at the rear of the railway station but on the way an even better depository presented itself. An open storm drain. There was nobody about and it was only the work of seconds to dump the blood-sodden sack into the gaping hole. He pulled the sledge another half mile before dumping it and going home. He had learned a salutary lesson and never again did he attempt a murder in a place where it could be traced back to him or where he had to run the unnecessary risk of hawking the body through the city streets.

Andrei Chikatilo continued cutting a bloody swathe across Russia for eight years. The police rushed around arresting anyone who came across their path who they could place within 50 miles of the latest murder site. Some of those who were arrested even confessed to the murders which had become the hottest news in the country. Those queuing up to confess had become so numerous that the police had a questionnaire which they were required to fill in before they could be given leave to be interrogated by a detective. This listed a number of questions that only the real killer could answer. Most failed this test. Those that scraped through were then subjected to a second barrage of questions. In the eight years that Chikatilo stalked the streets the police

estimated that 500,000 men were questioned. The only time they got near to Chikatilo was when he was picked up after the killing of Yelena Zakotnowa, his very first victim. If the detectives investigating the case had been more diligent in their work or even if the parents of the children he had molested earlier had reported the attacks, little Yelena might have been the only victim of Chikatilo's blood lust. As it was there were at least 50 cases that the police were aware of initially. Chikatilo added another dozen to their tally and confessed that there were probably more but as he had never kept a written record he was unable to give them a figure with any degree of certainty that it was correct. That he was caught at all was due to the unswerving persistence of one man, Detective Inspector Victor Burakow. He dismissed the opinions of the other detectives who from time to time took on the investigation. He dismissed the idea of members of a Satanic Cult being the culprits, it didn't fit the facts. Nor did he believe it was a gang of homosexuals running amok and performing bloody rites over the butchered corpses. The connections with the gory murders in London's Whitechapel a century earlier were similarly dismissed. Those who hadn't seen the bodies maintained that the murderer had to be a doctor because of the skilful way that the sexual organs had been removed. Another hint that Jack the Ripper was back. But Burakow had seen the bodies and the terrible mutilations and was well aware that the cuts and slashes were not the anatomical incisions of a surgeon's knife but the results of a frenzied attack. Semen specimens had shown conclusively that there was only one person taking part in the crimes but knowing that was as good, or bad, as knowing nothing. As the score of the distinctive crimes mounted, Burakow called in a noted psychologist and asked him to give him an idea of the type of man for whom they were searching. After examining all the known facts he came up with a description that certainly fitted the killer. Burakow wasn't going to be able to check this until he had got the killer behind bars. But it did give him a few pointers and at that stage of the investigation anything was acceptable. It was not inspired detective work of the Sherlock Holmes brand that wrote finish to Chikatilo's marathon murdering spree but systematic police work. With bodies turning up all the time and no leads, it was decided to try a new avenue. Burakow noticed that a high percentage of the atrocities were committed near the electric railway line. It seemed reasonable to suppose that the killer travelled on this not only to pick up his victims but also to get himself out of town to a new location. It was decided to intensify scrutiny on the trains and at stations. They had no real description of the man to go on but the patrol officers were told to look for a man with either a boy or girl. This meant stopping thousands of innocent people but with no direct leads it was worth a try. Nothing happened for weeks and the experiment was about to be aborted. Then an officer watching a suburban station noticed a tall, thin man wearing spectacles and carrying a briefcase, come out of a wooded area by the side of the station and walk towards the station. Just short of the entrance there was a horse trough. The man stopped and washed his hands in it before entering the station. The officer asked for his documents and wrote in his note book 'Andrei Chikatilo.' He also noted that the man had a faint smudge of red on his cheek which might have been blood. He hadn't been given any instructions about what to do with the information he garnered so the startling news that he had seen a man with blood on his face was filed with the rest of the daily reports. When it at last filtered through to Burakow he knew that at last he had got the break he had been looking for. Chikatilo had been picked up early in the investigation and questioned but released. Now he was placed at the scene of a crime and he wasn't going to get out of this one.

When Chikatilo was arrested he came quietly. It was probably a scenario he had often thought about over the years. The moment when all his years of slaughter would catch up with him. After an initial skirmish or two, when he denied all knowledge of the killings, he decided to confess. His confession was so detailed that it took the investigating officers by surprise. He was able to clear up murders where they hadn't even thought he might be involved. Brought to trial Chikatilo put on a bizarre performance from dropping his trousers to singing Communist songs. Sometimes he confessed to murders that he had done but had gone undiscovered. Then he would retract statements about murders he had done. By the time the trial was over he was constantly in an eyeball-to-eyeball confrontation with the judge or being sent back to the cells. If he was hoping to get the court to declare him insane, he failed. It took a long time to sum up the testimony but only seconds to come to a verdict: guilty. That was on the 14th October 1992. A peculiarity of the Russian death sentence is that the only one who doesn't know about the time of execution is the one about to get it in the neck – literally. Chikatilo sat in his cell for two years wondering if the next time the guard opened the door he would be coming for him. He did put in an appeal of sorts but it was laughed out of court. Nobody was willing to be responsible for putting this monster back on the streets. Then at 8.30am on the 14th of February 1994, the Sandman came for him. He was taken from the cell and escorted to the execution room. He guessed what was coming and as they walked in through the door he managed a mumbled, 'Sorry'. No one bothered to ask him what he was sorry for. Was it that he had murdered so many children or because he had been caught and brought to the execution room? The officer designated to draw the line under Andrei Chikatilo's murderous career took out his pistol, put it to the back of the neck of the condemned man and pulled the trigger.

20
Tomas de Torquemada

In many ways the most horrendous serial killers in history have been State funded: the Jacobin Club of Maximilien Francois Marie Isidore de Robespierre and Adolf Hitler's Nationalsozialistische Deutsche Arbeiterpartei to name but two. Prime among these is the iniquitous Spanish Inquisition. An institution set up with the collusion of the Church to root out heretics. Heretics being anyone who happened to run foul of either the secular or ecclesiastic authorities and could have the evidence manipulated in such a way that it suggested they weren't 100% behind the Christian Church of God. This included Moslems, Jews and Hindus for a start and other denominations as they came within the scope of whoever was dealing out God's justice at the time. Although in its early stages the Inquisition was strictly a Catholic affair, in the latter stages similar, yet divorced, institutions wreaked havoc among the Protestant off-shoots with their very own Witch Finder General. But they were small beer, except to those unfortunate enough to fall into their fires, compared with the Inquisitor General. Most countries had their own Grand Inquisitor at one time or another. The only countries that didn't fall fully under the spell of the torture chamber and the purifying fire were England and Germany. The Inquisition was first called into official existence in the 13th Century by Pope Gregory IX, although there had been similar institutions for well over 100 years before that. It was a fairly haphazard affair, very often the 'justice' was administered by the local head of a monastery or an itinerant monk with ideas above his station. Even at this stage, there was a tendency to get the accused into the fire to save his soul without even the mockery of a trial. The guidelines laid down by the Pope were fairly elastic. A person, of either sex, could be brought before the Cleric without evidence, and be judged without recourse of appeal. In the early stages, the judgment would probably be no more severe than a flogging or the torture of having to wear a hessian shirt. The real frightener was being excommunicated. It might not carry a lot of weight now but then it meant that the soul would fry in Satan's pan for eternity. At this point, the Inquisition was mainly a Popish thing. The incumbent in Rome either looking the other way or sitting in as the mood took him. In Spain, the Inquisitional ideal was looked on with envy. As far as the authorities, lay and church were concerned, it had only one drawback – it was administered from the wrong country. There was little anyone could do about it until King Henry IV managed to fix his sister up with Ferdinand of Spain. Isabella had a fixation about the Inquisition, to her it was the instrument of God and the only practical way to assure his continued dominion on earth, and a handy tool for getting rid of anyone who disagreed with the Crown, especially the rich dissenters and nobles who might be getting too big for their boots. The fact that once they had come under suspicion of heresy their worldly goods and chattels could be divided up between State and Church was an added bonus. Ferdinand was not the sharpest poniard in a scabbard and listened to Isabella's fantasies of securing a place in heaven where they would be in a position to pop round to God's cloud for a chalice of sugar if they ran out on a Saturday night. He listened and went along with her scheme to improve the neighbourhood. They sent emissaries to the new pope, Sixtus IX and flattered him into granting them a franchise on the Inquisition for Spain. Isabella had already sorted out a rich, ethereal, middle-aged man to take over the administration, Tomas de Torquemada. Tomas was born in 1420 in Torquemada, the town which had provided the name for his semi-illustrious family. His father, Pedro Fernandez was minor nobility and he had an uncle, Juàn, who was the Cardinal of Sisto. Although his father was inclined towards the gallant life and liked nothing more than a Saturday morning spent in a misty field sticking his rapier in some careless individual who he thought had insulted him, or gambling the night away in the palace of a mate, it was not the sort of calling that interested young Tomas. He was more interested in Uncle Juàn, at least in the sort of pious lifestyle to which the older man laid claim. He swallowed the idea of limpiez – pure blood untainted by the less noble races. He firmly believed that he was one of the privileged and aimed to be the most pure of the pure. His purity even extended to his sister. When his father finally died and left Tomas in charge of what was left of the family fortune, his first act was to send his sister to the convent of St Dominic and curry favour with his superiors by giving them what was left of his inheritance. Just to show how devoted he was to the life of poverty and self-denial, he refused to eat meat and always wore a sackcloth vest next to his skin. He was a brilliant scholar and was always pushing out tracts that proved the truth of the Immaculate Conception or some other dogma of the church which he believed was not taken seriously enough by those without the advantage of his noble birth or direct link to God. He might have stayed just a pain in the butt to those unfortunate enough to live in his parish if he hadn't been asked to hear the confessions of the Infanta Isabella. It wasn't a big deal at the time, Isabella was just a ward of a noble family, bored and more than happy to lap up the conceit and fervour of the young pastor. Then she was gone. It looked as if Tomas would spend the rest of his life as

Prior of the Monastery of Santa Cruz in Segovia. Then he discovered a terrible secret. Something that for him was so heinous it flipped his mind. Researching his family history he discovered that his Grandfather had married a Jew. Instead of being of the limpiezia, he was a mongrel. The offspring of a dreaded conversa. From that moment on, he devoted his life to cleaning the stain from his escutcheon. He hid his dread secret so well and practised such fervour in pursuit of God's work, that Sebastian of Olmeda was heard to remark that Tomas was, 'a scourge of heresy, a light of Spain, the Saviour of his country and an honour to his Order.' He was so pious that the Queen of Spain's frequent trips to the monastery to discuss outstanding matters of religious importance where assumed to be of a divine rather than a base nature. So when Isabella finally got the Pope's approval to set up a virtually autonomous branch of the Inquisition in Spain, she remembered the fervent priest of her youth and called him to court. He was now 58 years of age and practically unknown outside his little corner of Castile. It needed the Pope's approval to get Tomas blessed in his new appointment but Isabella was sure the Pontiff wasn't going to give her proposed Inquisitor General the thumbs down. Pope Sixtus IX was beholden to Tomas's Uncle Juàn for his promotion to minor Godship with the gift of popish infallibility. Even without this bit of ecclesiastical insider trading, Tomas had all the qualities demanded of the appointment. And he had backed up Uncle Juàn's claim of infallibility for the Pope with long, strenuously argued tracts that God had meant the earth to be an arbour of Saints under the benign administration of God's anointed Royals, Isabella and Ferdinand, and his representative on earth, Pope Sixtus. Once the horse-dealing was out of the way, Isabella and Ferdinand agreed that the headquarters should be set up in Castile. Although Torquemada was the managing director of the new enterprise, he set up a couple of deputies to undertake the establishment of the Inquisition in its new home. Miguel Morillo and Juàn de San Martin tortured their way through the local residents for just under two years. Then the Pope asked for them to be replaced when he got a flurry of letters from church patrons complaining that the Inquisitors were getting a little heavy-handed and forgetting their place. After all was said and done, they weren't there to have a go at the nobles – were they? Not wanting to find the Pope in the camp of those opposing the strictures of the Inquisition, Torquemada promised to calm the situation by taking over the administration of the quest to 'out' sinners and heretics into his own refined hands. The Pope breathed a sigh of relief. Obviously a cultured and well-connected man such as Tomas was not going to give him any trouble.

During the time that Morillo and San Martin had been administering the rack and flame, Torquemada had plenty of time to consider what the aims and objectives of the Grand Inquisition were. And what should be the penalties handed out to those who broke the rules. In 1482, he published his 28 Articles as a guide to Inquisitors. On the face of it, the 28 sins weren't that bad if you weren't a recent converso, a Jew who had converted to Christianity, or a morisco, a Moor who had done the same thing. The majority of Jews and Moors had converted because they were told if they didn't they would lose everything they had, wouldn't be able to do business and would have to do penance for worshipping in the wrong temple. Many of the more enlightened Jews and Moors, given 30 days to comply with the new regulations, folded their tents and went off to seek security elsewhere. Those that converted found their position hardly better than they would have found it without converting. Even the limited freedom they had won through conversion was soon swept away when Torquemada took over the job. The Priesthood were not immune from finding themselves being put to The Question. It was quite easy for the clergy to fall under suspicion. Just being sympathetic to a person later 'proved' to be a heretic could do the trick. Surprisingly fornication and sodomy were not considered a good

enough reason to get Torquemada on the vengeance trail. Sixtus himself was a well-known sexual swordsman and he still retained some authority in the Religious world. 'The Question' that was put to those accused of heresy was always the same. 'Are you guilty of heresy?' The answer was also always the same, 'Yes'. This was not because the officers detailed to arraign the evil-doers before the examiners were infallible but because just to be accused was enough to seal the fate of the accused – and very often the accuser as well.

In many ways the Inquisition set up the model for many Fascist states of the future. Arrests were usually made at night. The accused were frog-marched back to the examination building and brought immediately before the bench of the examiners. The Office was lit only by candles which flickered on the faces of the Inquisitors and made the statues of the Madonna and Christ seem to come to life. The examiners wore white cassocks topped off with intimidating black hoods. They were sat at a black-swathed table set with candles and crucifixes. Each Inquisitor had an open Bible in front of him which he read silently throughout the arraignment of the prisoner. The charges were read out by a lay member of the Inquisition. When he had finished, another Inquisitor, dressed entirely in black, would come forward and ask the prisoner if he confessed to his crimes against God. As there had been no mention of what the man, woman or child, was being charged with up to this point, the prisoner would ask what his crimes were. This was mistake number one and one that would be repeated regularly throughout the interrogations. Just to help the prisoner from damning his soul further by telling lies, the court would then introduce the Silence of God. This was an instrument that was inserted into the mouth. It had a screw attachment which when turned drove a wedge shaped piece of wood into the mouth and widened it until the jaws were just short of being unhinged. This was a very effective gag.

The following day the prisoner was again brought before the court. After several hours with his jaw at

Tomas de Torquemada presided over more than 200,000 executions of heretics.

breaking point, the heretic, for this is what he was by now, found it difficult to answer the simple questions put to him. Such as name, address, did he have any enemies and was he a good Catholic? If he was unable to reply, this was taken as dumb insolence. The Question was then put to him. This usually was enough to get the malfunctioning jaws into gear; the accused would try to get across the fact that he was willing to co-operate with the Inquisitors without them going to all the bother of heating up the branding irons. It was too late. The Inquisitors had been warned by Torquemada that this would happen and that it was all inspired by the devil trying to divert justice. The fact that they had suddenly found their voice was enough to confirm that they were up to no good. They were taken back to their cell where there were others who had fallen foul of the system and were further along the road to redemption. They bore witness to this with their broken and mutilated limbs. The next day the accused would again be taken before his accusers and the Inquisitors. Again, he would be asked to confess to his, or her, sins. By this time they were willing to confess to anything that would let them avoid the torture that would follow: the euphemistically named Question. Torquemada had foreseen this eventuality and warned his men to steel their hearts against the pitiful attempts of the accused to get out from under.

The prisoner was then taken to the room where The Question was to be put and shown the tools of the Torturer's art. Just in case they didn't get the point of the instruments used for the Question, they were shown in operation. Then, Torquemada or whoever was presenting the Question would say a little prayer suggesting that the accused should give up his evil ways and come willingly back into the love of God. By now, the accused was more than willing to go along with this suggestion. Unfortunately, that was not good enough. Torquemada was well aware of the wiles of the devil. It was too easy just to say you're sorry and then go back to your evil ways. So the torture began. By Torquemada's

own law, The Question could only be put once. If the questioned was answered truthfully, that was it. However, like all laws made by man there was a loophole. Although The Question could only be put once, there was nothing against a session going into recess and getting back to it later, and there was no restriction on how many times a session could be recessed. So the accused knew that the torture would go on until a miracle happened or he was tossed into the purifying fire. The Question usually started with the accused's hand being held on a block and a finger being severed. This was a sort of bookmark for the torturer. It made it easy for him to know where he was up to without either the fatigue of remembering or having to look it up in the records. The accused would then be strapped to a bench and his mouth forced open with wedges. A piece of thick cloth would then be placed over the face and water poured on it. The weight of the soaked cloth would assure that as the asphyxiated man frantically tried to draw breath, the cloth would slide inexorably down his gullet. When he was on the point of suffocation, the cloth would be removed and Torquemada would shuffle forward with a pained expression and explain that if only the sinner would see the Light of God and confess his sins his soul would be saved and he would be worthy of God's love. Eagerly, the wretch would take him at his word and confess to anything that came into his mind. It was never good enough. Even though Torquemada or whoever was taking his place, promised the end of their pain if they confessed, their confessions were never believed and the next phase would start. The accused's thumbs would be tied tightly together behind his back. A rope would be tied to this and stretched over a pulley. Gradually, the slack was taken up. The Inquisitor stood in front of the sufferer and gently asked him to confess. Again, the pain demented person would desperately cast around for crimes that he hadn't so far confessed with the fast disappearing hope that he might come up with something satisfactory. It was a forlorn hope. When the

Inquisitor was tired of doing God's work for the day he declared a recess. Gave the tortured person a blessing and staggered wearily off, happy in the knowledge that the tiresome and exhausting work he had to do was all in a good cause. The tortured was put back in the cells with the rest of the sufferers to groan away another fitful night wondering what the morning would bring. Business for the overworked Inquisitors was so brisk that they couldn't continue the questioning on a regular basis and those accused of defying God often had their state of heathenism prolonged by the simple fact that Torquemada and his gang just couldn't get around to saving an accused soul through pressure of business.

Day Two started as The Question was meant to go on. Finger number two would be lopped off to mark the passage of time. Torquemada would then have the heretic strapped to a table, say a little prayer over the bound figure and then ask gently if the accused had anything to confess. He had plenty and Torquemada would listen attentively before waving the torturer forward to do his work. Fastening hot pincers through the fleshy part of the chest and hoisting the body up on pulleys was another recommended torture. The heated points formed a hard shell in the flesh so that when the body was hoisted up the flesh didn't tear and, literally, let the body off the hook. Piercing the body also left a handy hole for introducing other instruments of torture. Tearing the teeth out was practically therapeutic after some of the ordeals. Like the ordeal by rat. In this torture small rats or mice were placed on the stomach of a prostrate figure. Then a metal implement which looked like an upturned pudding basin was carefully insulated so that it wouldn't come into contact with the bare flesh and strapped over the top of the hungry rats. Heat was then applied to the metal bowl. Frantically, the rats tried to get away from the heat and burrowed into the soft flesh beneath their feet. Before they could gnaw the accused to death they were retrieved. The tortured person was then sent back to his cell to contemplate the offence he had given God with his constant obstinacy

and perfidy. The next time the accused was sent for it was back to the old routine. Another finger, or if The Question was in its advanced stage, a toe was cut off. Maybe an hour or two on the rack to loosen things up and then maybe pins through the sides of the eye or maybe the head screw. This was just a metal band with a turnkey. The band was adjusted around the temples and the screw tightened a fraction of an inch at a time. With a patient operator this could last for hours. It was guaranteed to bring forth a lot of confessions that the tortured hadn't thought of before and Torquemada deemed this to be a great help in delivering the evil-doer from the arms of Satan.

After all this, it was getting extremely difficult to find a sensitive and relatively undamaged piece of flesh. The nervous system had shut down to such an extent that a bone broken here or a white hot iron there were bringing diminishing results. Rest periods were declared when the accused could sit and fester in the cell and contemplate the future. Those areas that were not about to drop off or were too infected to have working nerve ends had time to recover. Suspension of torture on the physical plane did not mean that the tortured could enjoy a rest in the lap of his or her fellow sufferers. Far from it. It was a time for the learner Inquisitors to get on the job. They gave the accused no rest. Day and night they bombarded them with the same questions they had been getting while under physical torture. After a week of being hounded, they were almost grateful when they were hauled back to the examination room. At least there they could get a few minutes of unconsciousness now and then. Finger-cutting and suspending with the arms up the back were now part of the daily routine. When the examiner wanted to knock off for a well-earned cup of tea, the victim was strung up and left to consider what sins he hadn't confessed while they refreshed themselves. In the latter stages of The Question, the Boot would be called into operation. This was kept back because once this had been slipped on to the foot, there was no Prince Charming to kiss it better.

The Boot was nothing more than a vice. Its purpose was slowly to crush the foot. When the Boot was removed, the foot was no longer capable of performing its duty and the victim had to be carried everywhere. Which was a little tiring after a hard day's torturing and maiming. If the Inquisitors still thought there was some mileage in the mass of suppurating and crushed wedge of humanity in front of them, they would now get really personal.

Evisceration was a skilled job to be performed only by the most expert torturer. The object of this charming practice was to show just how far the Inquisition was willing to go in the performance of their duty to save souls. The abdomen was carefully slit open and the entrails raked out and placed between the disembowelled's legs. Burning brands were then introduced into the cavity. When this proved effective – or even ineffective, nobody was a lot interested in the outcome by this time – the innards were stuffed back into place and the belly roughly stitched up. This operation required the greatest skill because it was considered a terrible sin if an accused died while in the arms of the church. Death was in the domain of the civic authorities. Even the most robust constitution could only survive a certain amount of torture and here again the skill of the Inquisitor came into play. He had to be sure that when his man was delivered up to the justice department, the sinner was still fit for the final act. This usually meant a few days rest before the main event. Although Torquemada was considered by those few outside his sphere of authority to be a dedicated man with a Godly mission, he was less respected by those who were liable to get the night call and the morning finger-chopping ritual. Several attempts at assassination failed and Torquemada replied by sending his men out on to the streets and by-ways with instructions to pick up everyone committing the ungodly act of walking around in broad daylight. They were all put to The Question and then passed on to the lay authorities for sentencing. This was a little irksome but it had to be done that way. The Church, and therefore the Inquisition, was an Institution of Love. What they did was for the good of, in the long run, mankind. In the short run, the soul of the heretic. They were not in the business of killing heretics but of saving souls. It was just unfortunate that when they had finished with the wrecked body and handed it over to the secular arm, that arm insisted on burning the poor, unredeemed body. Shades of the Sanhedrin and Jesus Christ.

The executions, usually by burning or if the alleged heretic was extremely lucky or knew someone who was inclined to do him a favour, by garrotting or decapitation, always took place on a Holy day. Unless the miscreant elected to become obstreperous and die on an unholy day. Then there was a quick ecclesiastical scrum and the day that he died was billed as an 'extraordinary'. The day before the Holy day, the heretics were dragged before the full chapter of the Inquisition and had to wait in silence while the charges and the punishment were read out for each of the accused. If anyone spoke or uttered a soft groan during the proceedings, they were hauled from the chamber and hung from the wall outside the door as a warning to others. Not hanged hung. That would have been too easy. Suspension by the thumbs was thought appropriate at this time. Although it was accepted that if the accused survived the torture the death penalty would automatically be passed, it was not always so. Sometimes, for some inexplicable reason, a sinner would be spared the fire. This usually meant the few to live would provide the 'warm-up' for the anticipated audience. They would be driven through the streets naked and thrashed violently with metal-tipped cat o'nine tails. Surviving meant that they could now watch as their homes were stripped of anything valuable and then either razed to the ground or taken under the protection of one of the holy orders endorsed by the Inquisition. The indignity of being whipped through the streets naked was spared those who were about to die. They were forced to wear a long tunic made out of sacking. Those who had not recanted the confession of their sins had the symbol of the Inquisition upside down and as an act of mercy would be strangled before being put on the fire. There were not many of these because the dead did not give such a good performance as the living. Women especially were not afforded the mercy of the garrotte. It was thought that their higher pitched screams were designed to strike even more terror into the heart of the condemned – if that were possible. Those who stood by their innocence and were condemned to burn in the flames did not lack an opportunity to confess their sins and have their sentence commuted to death by strangulation. Then they would be burnt at the stake. Every step of the way there were two hooded priests begging them to confess their sins and go to God with a pure heart. The same old problem still existed. The Priest's clients still had no idea to what they were supposed to confess and by this time had run out of inspiration. To most of them Death was a welcome visitor. Just so there would be no last minute mistakes, these recalcitrants wore the badge of the Inquisition the right way up.

Behind the condemned came the Inquisitors and Priests led by Torquemada surrounded by his well-trained personal bodyguard. These were hand-picked from the army and had sworn to lay down their life for the Inquisitor General. Torquemada insisted on being present whenever he could and always took a keen interest in the preparations. Sometimes he would go among the condemned himself and plead with them to confess their sins so that he could save them from their cruel fate by interceding with the lay authorities on their behalf. He was sad to find that all those to whom he was offering salvation either insisted that they were innocent or pleaded with him to tell them what their crimes were so that they could confess to them. Torquemada repeatedly implored the State executioners to show mercy on those who had fallen from God's Light. The Executioners knew better than to take him at his word. They preferred to be one of those beating the prisoners towards their final agonising destruction than to join

them under the whip. When the procession finally arrived at the place of execution, the prisoners were made to stand facing the stakes to which they were going to be tied and incinerated. This was carnival time for those who so far had escaped the zeal of the Inquisition. They were allowed to run riot among the broken hulks, linked to each other by nooses around their neck and often tied to the corpse of another heretic who had tried to escape God's justice by dying at an inappropriate time. Rotten fruit and stones thrown with cruel accuracy were considered small beer. Catching light to a beard or hair was more fun. Or beating with flails. The Inquisitors would sit back and watched with pained expressions on their austere faces but did nothing to mitigate the pain of those about to be cast into the flames. When the spectacle became repetitive and the tormentors had run out of fresh ideas, at a nod from Torquemada, the guards would move in and beat the audience back into line. Various priests, in rising order of supremacy, would then face the condemned and rant at them for making the work of the church so difficult. Warning them of the fire of hell that would undoubtedly be their destiny if they didn't confess their sins. When Torquemada had heard enough and he felt it was the right time to get on to the next stage he stood up and held out his hands. His men would blast forth on their trumpets and silence fell over the crowd. Torquemada would then go into a long and involved speech explaining why he had to take such repressive measures to defend God and how those awaiting execution were making the job very difficult. When the time was ripe, he would again walk along the line of prisoners and sometimes single someone out to be saved. At least that was the inference. He would call the Captain of the Lay guard and plead with him to let the selected person go. Stoically, the Guard refused to be persuaded. Wringing his hands in distress Torquemada would beg the man's forgiveness and return to his seat. The crowd fell to its knees as Torquemada, arms raised in benediction, would plead with God not to disown the souls of the sinners but to bring them to salvation in his Holy Light. That was the signal for the executioner to drag the condemned on to the scaffold and bind them to the posts set up there. Once that was secure, they went to those being granted the Blessing of strangulation and did their work. This could sometimes take a long time. While this was going on, the Priests hurried about from one soon-to-be-charcoaled victim to the next, begging them to come into the Arms of their Creator with a confession on their lips. They were too busy to wait for an answer. Finally, the moment came for what Torquemada and the crowd had been waiting. The Executioners lit their brands and came to the Priests and begged forgiveness for what they were about to do. Then Torquemada, with a becoming show of reluctance, gave the executioners absolution, begged them once more to show mercy and then sat eagerly watching the entertainment.

It has been estimated that during Tomas de Torquemada's tenure of office over 200,000 souls were consumed in the flames of his fire. Of those at least half were under the direct control of the Inquisitor General himself, Tomas Torquemada.

In spite of many attempts to assassinate him, so powerful was his image that they all came to naught.

21
Alexander Pearce

Ten Little Native-Americans, as the Agatha Christie Rep Company's staple drama is now called to satisfy the strictures of political correctness, was played out in a suitably macabre and deadly fashion in the Australian Outback of 1822. It wasn't the full count but this wasn't the fault of Alexander Pearce. He just ran out at seven. He did make a second attempt to reach the full count but still fell just short. The story of mayhem began in a village just outside Cork. Alexander was born the second of seven children to a dye washer. His father was a soldier but after he married Alexander's mother his appearances on the scene only preceded another pregnancy and then he disappeared and was not heard from again. By the time Alex was 14, he had only one surviving sibling, his elder sister and when she married, it left him the sole supporter of his arthritic, old beyond her years, mother. He did his best to support her but Ireland was not the best place for a wild boy and an ailing mother to try to survive at that time. Alexander wanted to run off to England and join the army but he didn't like to leave his mother so he started stealing to supplement the pittance he was being tossed for cleaning out the dye vats. The red dye sank into his skin and even then he was laughingly referred to as 'Bloody Pearce'. A name he was going to earn for real in later life. He wasn't a good thief and was caught on a number of occasions when he tried to steal food to feed them both. Each time he was caught he managed to get off with a caution or a kicking but the local JP was getting tired of punishing him without being able to bring him to heel. In 1819, he was brought before him once again, this time for stealing six pairs of shoes and several domestic items from a hardware store. When it had been necessities like bread or potatoes, the Magistrate had been prepared to be lenient. Now that his sights had turned to non-essentials like shoes, the JP was determined to bring down the full rigour of the law. Alexander was sentenced to seven years transportation to the Colonies. Transportation was often the alternative to the death sentence and not to be taken lightly. Ten years later, a boy of nine was hanged for stealing a cupful of paint. So, by the lore of the time, the young Alexander was being handed down the equivalent of capital punishment. There was very little chance that having once been committed to the Colonies he would ever see Ireland again. For one thing, the regime was not designed to nurture the weak and for another, the most strenuous work was handed out to the convicts who were coming to the end of their sentence. The philosophy behind this was that they would soon be leaving and of no further use as slave labour so they might as well be used up while they were available.

Marquarie Harbour, the penal colony on Van Diemen's Land, was one of the worst camps with a military commander who was well aware that his chances for promotion were not good. Army men who ended up commanding a penal colony were little more than prisoners themselves. It was the alternative to being cashiered with ignominy. Officers guilty of an offence were able to take the command if they had no means of support in the civilian world.

What was worse was that Pearce knew that he was going to be lucky to survive. He was always in trouble and he had already received three extra years on his sentence. He narrowly escaped being hanged on a couple of occasions and he knew that the next time he was in trouble, regardless of the offence, he would be used as target practice by the guards and then strung up so that the report could truthfully say that he had been hanged for his misdemeanours. He had attracted some of the hard men of the camp around him, all of whom doubted that they would ever live to see the outside world again. Pearce persuaded them that their only hope of survival was to break out. It wasn't particularly difficult. In fact, the Governor quite enjoyed the manhunt that ensued. Pearce wanted to rob the soldiers of their sport.

With his seven companions he stole a boat and under cover of darkness, rowed across the bay and disappeared into the thick forest. Pearce hoped that the boat wouldn't be missed at first and the search would begin in the opposite direction and give them a few hours start. It was a long hard day battling through the undergrowth after a sleepless night and as the sun set they huddled together in a clearing and for the first time gathered together their resources. There wasn't much. Pearce had a piece of stale bread and some dried meat. Matthew Travers had a knife and a loaf of bread. Greenhill had managed to hide away an axe when he was on a work party and had retrieved it before leaving, Dalton, Bodenham and Mathers had a few scraps of food. Two other convicts, Rudge and Betts had joined them at the last minute but they had come totally unprepared. But they weren't downhearted. Pearce had a plan. They would keep to the coastline and head east. There they would come across some of the bigger settlements, maybe eventually reach Darwin and disappear into the crowds of immigrants and ex-soldiers who were settling there.

The next day began well. They were alive and there was no sign of a hunting party. They headed along the coast and for the next couple of days and managed to make reasonable headway. Then they hit swamp. Not just swamp but crocodile-filled swamp. It meant they had to turn inland. That wasn't too bad. It would mean that it would be a couple more days before they would reach civilisation. But who cared? They were free! Two days later they were hopelessly lost. They decided to head back to where they hoped the coast might be. They hit hills and dense forests. And they were out of food. None of them had any idea how to live off the land and they nearly poisoned themselves trying to eat berries and roots. It was 10 days since their meagre rations had been depleted and fever and starvation was weakening them to a degree where they could hardly move. It was obvious that drastic methods had to be adopted if they were to survive. Pearce, Mathers and Greenhill went into a huddle. Democratically, they voted that for the sake of the whole, a member of the party had to be sacrificed. And it would have to be Dalton. The reason Dalton was chosen was that back in the penal colony he had been one of the prisoners used to whip other prisoners when they committed a misdemeanour. It wasn't a popular job but somebody had to do it. Understandably, they decided it would be best not to tell Dalton his fate. Once he was asleep, Greenhill crept up on him with his trusty axe and with one stroke sliced off his head. The sound woke the others and they stared wide eyed as Mathers moved in and cut himself a few steaks. None of the others joined in as Mathers and Greenhill built a fire and sat down to a meal. Replete, they lay down to sleep. The others found sleep harder to come by and by the morning Rudge and Betts who had never really been a part of the Pearce gang, were gone. They decided that being whipped for escaping was better than waking up without a head.

By the following morning, when Mathers cut up the body of his ex-comrade so that it would be easier to carry, the others had convinced themselves that, now that he was dead, it would be churlish to let him give his life for nothing. They accepted the share out and went on their way cheerfully munching on a piece of the

Alexander Pearce was the last one left standing after the cannabilistic march through Northern Australia.

body. Now they were down to five, it would be easy to last out until they reached a farm or somewhere they could steal food. Unfortunately, they were still lost and going around in circles. When they were in the trees they couldn't keep in a straight line and when they emerged on a plain, the mountains always seemed in a different direction. This time when they ran out of food, the solution was easier. Bodenham carelessly allowed Greenhill to walk behind him. It was an opportunity that Greenhill wasn't going to pass up. As the axe split Bodenham's skull, the others were reaching out to snatch the choicer pieces. They decided to make camp for the day and discuss the situation. Pearce made Greenhill promise that he wouldn't use the axe again without first having a vote and letting serendipity decide who would provide lunch. They all nodded agreement but even as he agreed, Greenhill's hand tightened on his axe. Now they were only four, they assured each other, the extreme measures that had been forced on them by circumstances beyond their control, would not be needed again. But everyone made sure that they kept well clear of the axe man. Still they were lost and once again rations were running low. There was a half-hearted effort to try once more to find vegetable matter that would give them nourishment but it proved fatal for Mathers. While he was vomiting after trying yet another inedible piece of the verdant scenery, Greenhill seized his chance, crept up behind him and swung his axe. Mathers saw it coming and managed to duck to one side. The blade missed but the shaft hit the side of his head. Mathers was tough. He managed to grab Greenhill and stop him finishing the job. Pearce watched silently. He had long ago decided that if anyone was going to get through it was going to be him. He was happy to see the others engaged in a strength-sapping fight. Eventually, the combatants were exhausted. Now that the adrenaline rush had subsided the effects of the savage blow to his head took effect. Greenhill, still clutching his axe stood up and was about to finish him off when Pearce intervened. He told

Mathers that he was finished. He would never have the strength to continue their terrible journey. He suggested that Mathers should have a little time to himself to prepare for the inevitable. There was nothing Mathers could do. There was nothing he wanted to do. Already he could feel reality slipping away from him. He closed his eyes and this time Greenhill didn't miss.

The three, Pearce, Greenhill and Travers, struggled on, each jealously guarding the portion of Mathers that they had claimed for themselves. That night after they had eaten, they sat around their campfire and swore an oath that there would be no more cannibalism. They were friends and they would stick together until the bitter end. The bitter end came swiftly for Travers. Greenhill had now come to terms with his role. There was no need to go hungry when there was prime, fresh flesh walking beside you. Greenhill waited until they were crossing a stream and then as Travers was fully occupied dragging his exhausted body up the bank, laid his skull open with his axe. Now there were only two. They didn't bother to pledge their allegiance, they were both aware that sleep was going to be the killer. Greenhill had the axe but Pearce had the will. For days they staggered on. For a while they thought they might survive. They were out of the forest and on the pleasant foothills of the Engineer Mountains. It seemed to be the sort of place that homesteaders might settle. But they found no evidence of occupation. They walked warily, never venturing nearer than 20 yards of each other. They dare not sleep. The hot sun took its toll. They were afraid to stop in case they dropped off to sleep and presented an easy target for the other. Finally, Greenhill could take it no longer. He found himself a hollow that in his sleep-deprived state he thought impregnable, and settled down. His axe tightly clasped in his hands. Every few minutes he would jerk awake and look around. Pearce was in no hurry. He wouldn't allow himself to sit down and rest in case he too fell asleep. An hour went by. Greenhill was now fast asleep. He no longer had his waking spasms. Greenhill had his terrible axe but when

Travers had been killed, Pearce had claimed his knife. Pearce cautiously edged towards Greenhill. He was still six yards short when the sleeping man stirred and appeared to be about to awaken. Pearce discarded caution and dived in. His body landed on top of the axe so that Greenhill could not have wielded it even if he had the chance. With one vicious slash Pearce sliced open the sleeping man's throat. As he heard the last gurgling breath die away, Pearce relaxed. He was too exhausted to even roll off his victim's body. For the first time in a week, he slept. The next morning he built a fire and gorged himself on the body. He knew that if he didn't find food before he had finished getting his nourishment from the remains of Greenhill, he was a goner so he carried away as much as he could. A couple of days later he met a settler, Pat McGuire, who gave him food and pointed him in the direction of the nearest town.

Pearce managed to stay out of trouble for a couple of months but then he was spotted by an ex-convict who, hoping to claim a reward, turned him into the police. He was sent back to Marquarie Harbour where he confessed everything. It was so outrageous that the camp commander didn't believe a word of it. He ordered him to be flogged and thrown into solitary confinement. Pearce was little more than an animal now. When the guard came to feed him, he tore out his throat with his teeth and, with the prisoner, Thomas Cox, who had brought him his food, once more escaped. It was 13 months since his last escape. But this time he had a plan. He headed north hoping to make Port Dalrymple. He had brought along Thomas as fresh fodder. Three days after the escape, he cut the throat of Cox and fed. This time the pursuers guessed right and followed. Two days later they caught up with him as he was roasting one of Cox's legs on his fire. This time they were prepared to believe him.

Pearce was taken to Hobart, found guilty of the murder of Thomas Cox and executed. He seemed to be totally disinterested in what was happening to him and made no protest when he was taken to the place of execution. There is a grisly aftermath to this grisly tale. When Dr Crockett of the Hobart Colonial Hospital heard about Pearce, he claimed his head – 'for medical research'. He sawed off the top of the head, took out the brain and eyeballs and then boiled the head until all the flesh was stripped off. He kept it on his desk as a tobacco jar and conversation piece for a while. When he found something else that took his fancy, he sent the skull off to Dr Sam Norton of the Academy of Natural Sciences in Philadelphia where it joined hundreds of other skulls that had once housed a brain that had in some way differed from the brains of those around them – or maybe not.

22
The Pierrepoints

Whereas the basis for James Berry's satisfaction with his job of executioner was gastronomy, it seems that Albert Pierrepoint, the most prolific of all who excelled in the job, was in it for the travel opportunities it offered. He proudly stated that on a good day he could take a three o'clock flight from Dublin, and after a successful execution, be opening his pub, the appropriately named 'Help the Poor Struggler', at half past five.

The progress to Albert's pre-eminence as the foremost hangman in England started with the trade of his grandfather, Henry, or Harry – depends on how intimate you were with him. Harry was the local butcher in a small Yorkshire town on the fringes of York. When the city fathers were looking for a suitable man who would be readily available to work the rope they, naturally, went to see the butcher. They explained that they were planning an efficiency drive and were no longer content to be at the mercy of the Crown's peripatetic hangman and wanted someone who could carry out executions to their timetable and not his own. Harry was up for the job and founded a hanging dynasty that lasted for more than half a century and saw off some of the most flamboyant killers, traitors and thieves of the 19th and 20th Centuries. Harry was one of the old time 'string 'em up and let 'em swing' brigade. Public hangings had ceased in 1868, due mainly to the efforts of Sir Robert Peel who was appalled by the number of crimes that carried the capital sentence. Once he had whittled these down, it was natural to take another look at the

actual act and decide that State revenge was not a suitable subject for public entertainment. But old Harry Pierrepoint could remember the good old days when it was considered a public holiday when there was to be a hanging. And there was still a plethora of lively tales recounted about Jack Ketch who plied his fatal trade 100 years before that. Not that any respectable civil servant seeing off the enemies of the Queen (Victoria, that is) would have much sympathy with the old rascal. They considered that they had come a long way since then and liked to think of themselves on a par with city councillors and officers of the law. Jack Ketch was the reason that so much odium was attached to the office. He was the killing arm of Bloody Judge Jeffreys who was extremely efficient at passing the death sentence on anyone unlucky enough to appear before him. Efficiency was not one of the watch words of Jack Ketch. He was a bungling drunkard who seemed incapable of performing an execution without either making a botch of it or turning it into a tasteless side show. And if you are planning to slice someone's head from their shoulders, you would obviously prefer a melodrama to a Feydeau farce. This was a time when many executions were done with the axe. It was customary for the victim to give the axe man a tip so that he would make a swift and neat job. Ketch was well versed in taking the tip but seemed unable to direct the axe onto the proffered neck with any degree of accuracy. As Lord Russell, who was condemned for his part in a plot to kill James II, found to his cost. So drunk was Ketch that the first blow almost missed the

British hangman Albert Pierrepoint at home with his dog.
After his retirement, he stated that he couldn't see the point of hanging anyone. (Popperfoto)

aristocrat's neck entirely. All it did was lop off an ear and nick his neck. Russell was furious and complained that he wasn't getting his 10 guineas worth. Ketch mumbled an apology and took another drunken swing – and missed. It took three more shots finally to separate head from torso. But that was practically perfect for a Ketch killing, as the Duke of Monmouth found out when he was sent to visit Jack Ketch, in the aftermath of the Monmouth Rebellion, in 1685. Ketch thrashed away at the nobleman's neck without actually severing it completely. It was left to his assistant, when Ketch had exhausted himself, to leap in and finish the job with a knife. Ketch's notoriety had left an indelible stain on the role of executioner. His name was used as a bogeyman to scare naughty children and his effigy was enrolled into the Punch and Judy show. But Jack got his comeuppance after beating the wife of a baker to death and was hanged by his successor, John Price. Price was a man of the same ilk and was himself hanged on the same gallows a couple of years later.

One of Pierrepoint's more immediate predecessors was the man idolised by James Berry, William Calcraft. He was also a prize bungler but managed to put over an air of benign haplessness. By trade he was a cobbler and over his shop he had the legend – 'Boot and Shoe Mender' and then in a box at the side in much larger letters 'Executioner to Her Majesty'. He kept a menagerie of animals and was a fastidious dresser. He was the last incumbent of the office to be sworn in with the full Masonic-type oath. It was a day out for the Lord Mayor and a chance for the upright citizens to show their contempt for the man who was doing their bidding. Calcraft was called before a committee consisting of the Lord Mayor, the Sheriff of London, the London Marshal, the Governor of Newgate, a Judge and anyone else in need of demonstrating his superiority. Then with bells tolling and suitable solemnity he was given the right to kill, without the nicety of a double 0 number

– then driven from the presence of the upright citizens with cries of 'Begone villain'.

By the time Harry Pierrepoint was summoned from his butcher's shop, the ceremony had been dispensed with and it was just a question of willingness and money. The Pierrepoints opened and closed the final era in the trade of executioner. Harry Pierrepoint finally resigned in 1916 after topping 78 recalcitrants. He handed on the noose and leg-irons to his elder brother Tom, who had often been a willing assistant. Tom's approach was different from that of his younger brother. Harry had always tried to make his clients feel at home. A cheery word, a fleeting hand on the shoulder, a fitting solemnity. It was unlikely that the man standing on the trapdoor was impressed but it made the man pulling the lever a lot happier. Tom was more pragmatic. He was there to do a job. He didn't want to marry the person on the scaffold – just hang him and get back to the pub. His off-hand approach kept him in employment from 1916 until 1948. By then, he had the distinction of being Britain's longest-serving executioner with 102 drops to his credit. He had also risen to the position of head hangman. During the latter part of his tenure he had the help of his young nephew, Albert. Albert loved the job. He felt that in all of Britain there wasn't a man more blessed. He was the man who served the law in a capacity that really made a difference. He followed neither the friendly 'let's get on with it' attitude of Harry nor the 'it's all in a day's work' ethos of Tom. To Albert, it was a profession on a par with a lawyer or a surgeon. He brought time and motion techniques to the scaffold. He could settle a noose, put on a hood, tie the arms, pinion the legs and pull the lever in a swift 17 seconds.

Albert's big moment came at the end of the Second World War. The large throughput of Nazi war criminals at Nüremberg ensured that there would be a busy time for the executioner. The man who volunteered for the job was Master Sergeant John C

Tom Pierrepoint saw his tenure as Head Executioner as an ordinary job.

Woods. He hadn't any experience but there wasn't a scramble for the job and he expressed the correct sentiments and was eager to learn. Besides which, there wasn't a lot of sympathy for those on trial and if Wood's learning curve was a little flaccid who would care? Just how inefficient he was fell to criminals like Admiral Keitel, Ambassador von Ribbentrop and several other top Nazis to find out – the hard way. But he was building up a backlog so the Americans allowed the British Forces to appoint their own man. That man was Albert Pierrepoint. He soon had the execution yard running like a Ford assembly line and before long the backlog had been cleared and the Master Sergeant had learned a salutary lesson about the administration of capital punishment.

But Albert didn't have an easy time of it when it came to hanging the 'Beautiful Blonde Beast of Belsen' – Irma Grese. A rumour started that Albert and Irma were carrying on an affair in her prison cell. There was even a story that she had married him in front of a German Chaplain in an attempt to get her sentence reduced to life imprisonment instead of the dawn drop. This meant that Pierrepoint must have been a very fast worker. The prison records show that Albert was only in the prison where Grese was held for 32 hours and all of his conversations with her were through an interpreter. The only times he came within arm, or anything else, range was when he weighed and measured her and on that final morning when he spent a swift 17 seconds with her adjusting the noose and tying her arms behind her back. In his autobiography, *Executioner* he describes the thrilling moments leading up to the time he slipped the noose over her head. The night before she had spent in her cell singing Nazi songs with her mates, Elisabeth Volkenrath and Juana Bormann. When he met her beneath the noose, he thought she was a 'bonnie lass' and admired her for her beauty and dignity. As he went to pull the hood over her head, she gave him an enigmatic smile which haunted him for the rest of his life. He claimed that she

was the bravest woman, or man, he had ever broken the neck of. That's all right then.

Exhausted by his efforts in the cause of military justice, Albert returned to his pub a celebrity. Since the abolition of public hangings, the hangman had become an anonymous figure. More so since Tom had taken the last vestige of ghoulish glamour out of the trade with his phlegmatic approach. Now, Albert Pierrepoint was a name on everyone's lips. Well, at least everyone who had an interest in the follow-up to the ominous words intoned by the Judge, a black handkerchief on his wig, at the end of a trial: 'The sentence of this court is that you be taken hence to a place of execution and that you be hanged by the neck until you are dead: and that your body be afterwards buried within the precincts of the prison in which you were confined before your execution. And may the Lord have mercy on your soul – Amen.' The end of the Nüremberg executions was by no means the end of Albert as an efficient killing machine. He continued as executioner until the law was changed and he became redundant. Among those he helped on their way were Neville Heath who wrote to his mother from his condemned cell and apologised for being 'a damned unworthy son'. He had also strung up Ruth Ellis – 'The Last Woman to be Hanged in Britain'. It was this judicial murder that finally swung the waverers behind the move to abolish hanging. Her crime was simple. She fell in love with David Blakely, a racing car driver. She met him in a drinking club and for a while they were an item. She became pregnant and had a back street abortion. Blakely left her for another woman and in a highly emotional state, still suffering from the after effects of her abortion, she took a gun and shot him. Reprehensible but by no means deserving of the death penalty.

Albert Pierrepoint also did the business on Timothy Evans. He hanged for the murders of his wife and baby daughter, Beryl and Geraldine, in the notorious killing house of 10 Rillington Place. A couple of years later, Albert slipped the noose around

APPLICATION FOR SPECIAL TRANSFER RATE FOR

(No.) __1 set__ (Article) __Execution Apparatus__

FOR __War Office__ A. 1125/198 ____ 28 th April, 1952.

NOTE :— The following percentage should be added for wear and tear of tools, incidental expenses, etc., in the case of articles made in Prisons and Borstal Institutions: 10% Blacksmithing, Brush-making, Foundry Work and Tinsmithing. 7½% Power Loom Weaving and Printing. 2½% Baking, Knitting and Picking. 5% all other trades, unless otherwise ordered.

(Fractions of pence in the valuation should be worked to two places of decimals.)

Quantity	Description		Contract No.	Rate	VALUATION			RATE APPROVED		
					£	s.	d.	£	s.	d.
1 no	Box Execution	for	TR		2	2	1.46			
1	Block and Fall Tackle	for	C.P.		8	13	3.00			
1 no	Bag, sand.	for	T.R.		1	17	7.52			
2 no	Ropes 10' 6"	ea	C.P.	117/6	11	9	1.50			
1 set	Straps pinioning	ten	C.P.	181/6	-	18.	1.80			
1 no	Cap execution	ea	T.R.	10.26d	-	-	10.26			
1 no	Rod measuring	ea	C.P.	16/6	-	16	6.00			
2 no	Locks, pad	ea	C.P.	9/9-	-	19	0.15			
3 oz	Chalk(4 pieces)	100	C.P.	5/-	-	-	2.40			
2 oz	Wire copper	1b	C.P.	3/-½d	-	-	4.56			
2/3 oz	Twine seaming	1b	C.P.	3/7d	-	-	1.79			
1 no	Chain execution	ea	C.P.	42/6d	2	2	6.00			
1 no	Box Chain	for	T.R.		-	13	1.28			
2 no	Pyrothene Bags	ea	C.P.	1/3d	-	2	6.00			
4 Oz	Para: crystals	for	C.P.		-	1	0.00			
					29	16	5.72			
	5% tool				1	9	9.38		31	7
	Add 10% Departmental Charge				5	7	4.38			
					31	6	3.60			
	Collected.				35	3	10.19			

+ as A1125/190 of 24-8-50

2

S. Perigi. Stev

Evans' landlord, John Reginald Halliday Christie.

Albert retired to run his pub in 1956. In his autobiography he substantiated James Berry's thoughts on capital punishment. 'I do not believe that any of the hundreds of executions I have carried out has in any way acted as a deterrent against future murder. Capital punishment, in my view, achieves nothing except revenge.' It will be noted that he made this statement, however sincere, after he had strung up 530 men and 20 women.